ENDOCRINOLOGY RESEARCH AND C

SOMATOSTATIN

SYNTHESIS, MECHANISMS-OF-ACTION AND PHYSIOLOGICAL EFFECTS

ENDOCRINOLOGY RESEARCH
AND CLINICAL DEVELOPMENTS

Additional books in this series can be found on Nova's website
under the Series tab.

Additional e-books in this series can be found on Nova's website
under the e-book tab.

SOMATOSTATIN

SYNTHESIS, MECHANISMS-OF-ACTION AND PHYSIOLOGICAL EFFECTS

ALLISON ANDERSON

AND

TAYLOR MCANULTY

EDITORS

New York

For permission to use material from this book please contact us:
Telephone 631-231-7269; Fax 631-231-8175
Web Site: http://www.novapublishers.com

NOTICE TO THE READER

Additional color graphics may be available in the e-book version of this book.

Library of Congress Cataloging-in-Publication Data

ISBN: 978-1-62417-419-3
Library of Congress Control Number: 2012952791

Published by Nova Science Publishers, Inc. † New York

CONTENTS

PREFACE

Somatostatins (SST) form a family of cyclopeptides that are mainly produced by normal endocrine, gastrointestinal, immune and neuronal cells, as well as by certain tumors. By binding to G-protein-coupled receptors on target cells, SST act as neuromodulators and neurotransmitters, as well as potent inhibitors of various secretory processes and cell proliferation. In this book, the authors discuss the synthesis, mechanisms-of-action and physiological effects of somatostatins. Topics include the effects of somatostatin in animal models of retinal disease; radiolabelled somatostatin analogues for use in molecular imaging; somatostain analogs as a treatment for congenital hyperinsulinism; somatostain and its receptors in the mammalian cochlea; diagnostic accuracy of positron emission tomography with somatostatin analogues in gastroenteropancreatic and thoracic neuroendocrine tumors.

Chapter 1 – The neuropeptide somatostatin (somatotropin release inhibiting factor, SRIF) has been widely investigated in the retina, where it is localized to sparse amacrine cells and, in some instances, in a subset of ganglion cells. All five different SRIF subtype receptors (designated sst_1 through sst_5) are expressed in the mammalian retina, and their variegated expression patterns, together with the variety of signaling mechanisms activated by the different ssts, suggest that the somatostatinergic system may exert multiple actions on retinal neurons and on retinal physiology. For instance, SRIF, mostly acting through sst_2, functions as a positive factor in the retina by regulating retinal homeostasis and protecting neurons against damage. In particular, a considerable amount of experimental evidence has been gathered to show that sst_2 activation may effectively limit the expression of pro-angiogenic signals, thereby counteracting the growth of new, aberrant vessels that is typically seen, for instance, in diabetic retinopathy. In addition,

SRIF has been shown to protect retinal neurons from excitotoxic insults caused by excess of glutamate release. This condition is frequently associated with retinal ischemia, which is a common cause of severe retinal damage in different pathologies. Several studies have described potent protective actions of SRIF in the ischemic retina mediated by sst_2 activation. Taken together, these data support the notion that therapeutic strategies based on the use and implementation of SRIF analogues may be clinically relevant in different retinal diseases such as ischemic and diabetic retinopathies. This chapter reviews the literature concerning the advances in the research of the roles played by the somatostatinergic system in animal models of retinal disease.

Chapter 2 – Being able to monitor tumours and their response to treatment is essential in therapy planning. Somatostatin receptor (SSTR) positive tumours, there among neuroendocrine tumours, can be imaged by using radiolabelled somatostatin analogues. In the late 1980's the first radiolabelled somatostatin analogue was reported. A few years later the gamma emitting tracer which still is considered the golden standard, $[^{111}In\text{-}DTPA^0]$octreotide (OctreoScan), was introduced. From that point a number of analogues labelled with various nuclides for imaging techniques like scintigraphy, single photon emission computed tomography (SPECT) and positron emission tomography (PET) have been developed to obtain improved imaging properties. The five subtypes of SSTR (sst_{1-5}) are unequally distributed in SSTR-positive malignancies, and the structures of the somatostatin analogues are therefore varied to obtain high binding affinity for each. Development of PET octreotide tracers has made high resolution imaging possible. The positron emitting nuclide ^{68}Ga is conveniently obtained from an easy to handle $^{68}Ge/^{68}Ga$ generator. Several of the ^{68}Ga-labelled octreotide derivatives, like DOTA-TOC (DOTA-D-Phe^1-Tyr^3-octreotide), DOTA-TATE (DOTA-Tyr^3-octreotate) and DOTA-NOC (DOTA-1-Nal^3-octreotide), have superior pharmacological properties compared to OctreoScan. These derivatives can also be labelled with therapeutic nuclides like ^{90}Y and ^{177}Lu and consequently used as theranostic pairs.

The intention of this chapter is to give an overview of available somatostatin analogues labelled with radioactive isotopes and their use in molecular imaging. Focus will be made on analogues labelled with PET nuclides, ^{68}Ga in particular.

Chapter 3 – Congenital hyperinsulinism (CHI) is a functional disorder of insulin secretion. The long-term outcome of infants with CHI depends on the prevention of hypoglycemic episodes to avoid the high risk of permanent brain damage including psychomotor retardation, seizures, and learning disabilities.

In its diffuse severe form, it is traditionally treated with near-total pancreatectomy. However, even after this procedure normoglycemia is not always achieved, and many patients develop diabetes mellitus at puberty.

Human β-cells show a high expression of somatostatin receptors, particularly type 2 (SSTR2), and somatostatin directly suppresses insulin release. It was therefore hypothesized that somatostatin could be used as a therapeutic agent in CHI. This hypothesis was successfully tested as early as 1977, but clinical implementation was limited by the short half-life of native somatostatin. With the advent of the first somatostatin analog, octreotide, in the 1980's, a conservative approach to the treatment of CHI was developed, using octreotide administered subcutaneously by injection or through a pump, in combination with other medications (diazoxide, glucagon), as well as frequent or continuous feeding by means of a gastrostomy tube. Using this approach it is possible to achieve euglycemia, normal growth and good neurodevelopmental outcome, at least in some patients' groups. Potential side effects of treatment with somatostatin include cholelithiasis, impaired growth, and impaired thyroid function. However, the only side effect the authors usually encounter is asymptomatic cholelithiasis. Despite our success with the conservative approach, the treatment may pose a huge burden and be stressful for the patients and families. Recently, the authors and others reported successful treatment with the long –acting somatostatin analogs lanreotide acetate and octretide LAR, administered once-monthly, and resulting in simplification of daily care and improved quality of life.

Chapter 4 – Somatostatins (SST) form a family of cyclopeptides that are mainly produced by normal endocrine, gastrointestinal, immune and neuronal cells, as well as by certain tumors. By binding to G-protein-coupled receptors (SSTR1-5) on target cells, SST act as neuromodulators and neurotransmitters, as well as potent inhibitors of various secretory processes and cell proliferation. Little is known about the expression and function of the somatostatinergic system in the mammalian cochlea. The authors analyzed the expression of SSTR1-SSTR5 in the immature mammalian cochlea. The peak in the expression of SSTR1 and SSTR2 at mRNA and protein level is around the onset of hearing to airborne sound, at postnatal day (P)14. This suggests their involvement in the maturation of the mammalian cochlea. In immunohisochemical studies the authors demonstrated that all five receptors are expressed in the outer and inner hair cells (HCs) as well as in defined supporting cells of the organ of Corti (OC) in the adult mouse cochlea. A similar expression of the SST receptors in the inner and outer hair cells was found in cultivated P6 mouse OC explants. Interestingly, SST itself is not expressed in the mammalian cochlea, suggesting that SST reaches its receptors either trough the blood-labyrinthine barrier from the systemic circulation or via the endolymphatic duct from the endolymphatic sac. In order to learn more about the regulation of SST receptors, the authors used mice with either a deletion of SSTR1, SSTR2 or SSTR1/SSTR2. In SSTR1 knock-out (KO) mice, SSTR2 were up-regulated. In contrast, in SSTR2 KO mice, the expression pattern of SSTR1 was not altered compared to wild-type mice. In SSTR1/SSTR2 double knockout (DKO) mice, SSTR5 was up-regulated but SSTR3 and SSTR4 were down regulated. These findings provide evidence of a compensatory regulation in the mammalian cochlea as a consequence of a receptor subtype deletion. In addition, the authors observed reduced levels of phospho-Akt and total-Akt in SSTR1 KO and DKO mice as compared to wild type (WT) mice. Akt is likely to be involved in hair cell survival.

Most importantly, the authors found improved hair cell survival in somatostatin treated OC explants that had been exposed to gentamicin compared to those explants exposed to gentamicin alone. These findings propose that the somatostatinergic system within the cochlea has neuroprotective properties.

Chapter 5 – *Introduction:* Positron emission tomography (PET) using somatostatin analogues labelled with Gallium-68 is a valuable diagnostic tool for patients with neuroendocrine tumors (NETs).

Aim of our study is to review published data about the diagnostic performance of PET or PET/computed tomography (PET/CT) in patients with thoracic and/or gastroenteropancreatic (GEP) NETs.

Methods: A comprehensive computer literature search of studies published through October 2011 and regarding PET or PET/CT studies in patients with thoracic and/or GEP NETs was carried out.

Results: Sixteen studies comprising 567 patients were included in this review. The pooled sensitivity and specificity of PET or PET/CT with somatostatin analogues in detecting NETs were 93% (95% confidence interval [95%CI]: 91-95%) and 91% (95%CI: 82-97%), respectively, on a per patient-based analysis. The area under the ROC curve was 0.96.

Conclusions: In patients with suspicious thoracic and/or GEP NETs, PET or PET/CT with radiolabelled somatostatin analogues demonstrated high sensitivity and specificity. These accurate techniques should be considered as first-line diagnostic imaging methods in patients with suspicious thoracic and/or GEP NETs.

In: Somatostatin   ISBN: 978-1-62417-419-3
Editors: A. Anderson and T. McAnulty © 2013 Nova Science Publishers, Inc.

Chapter 1

EFFECTS OF SOMATOSTATIN IN ANIMAL MODELS OF RETINAL DISEASE

*Davide Cervia and Giovanni Casini**

Department for Innovation in Biological, Agro-food and Forest Systems
(DIBAF), University of Tuscia, Viterbo, Italy

ABSTRACT

The neuropeptide somatostatin (somatotropin release inhibiting factor, SRIF) has been widely investigated in the retina, where it is localized to sparse amacrine cells and, in some instances, in a subset of ganglion cells. All five different SRIF subtype receptors (designated sst_1 through sst_5) are expressed in the mammalian retina, and their variegated expression patterns, together with the variety of signaling mechanisms activated by the different ssts, suggest that the somatostatinergic system may exert multiple actions on retinal neurons and on retinal physiology. For instance, SRIF, mostly acting through sst_2, functions as a positive factor in the retina by regulating retinal homeostasis and protecting neurons against damage. In particular, a considerable amount of experimental evidence has been gathered to show that sst_2 activation may effectively limit the expression of pro-angiogenic signals, thereby counteracting the growth of new, aberrant vessels that is typically seen, for instance, in diabetic retinopathy. In addition, SRIF has been shown to protect retinal neurons from excitotoxic insults caused by excess of

* Corresponding author: Giovanni Casini, PhD, DIBAF, University of Tuscia, Largo dell'Università snc, blocco D, 01100 Viterbo – Italy; E-mail: gcasini@unitus.it.

glutamate release. This condition is frequently associated with retinal ischemia, which is a common cause of severe retinal damage in different pathologies. Several studies have described potent protective actions of SRIF in the ischemic retina mediated by sst_2 activation. Taken together, these data support the notion that therapeutic strategies based on the use and implementation of SRIF analogues may be clinically relevant in different retinal diseases such as ischemic and diabetic retinopathies. This chapter reviews the literature concerning the advances in the research of the roles played by the somatostatinergic system in animal models of retinal disease.

INTRODUCTION

The mammalian retina contains a defined, small number of principal cell types organized in distinct layers. Its ordered laminar organization, the discrete output and accessibility have promoted a high quantity of experimental studies that have led to an understanding of retinal circuitry and retinal physiology. The retina is part of the central nervous system and it is separated at the same time, allowing easy experimental approaches. In addition, it displays the complexity typical of the brain while having an ordered, layered structure that is conserved throughout its extension. In virtue of these features, the mammalian retina has been extensively used as an experimental model of the central nervous system.

Five principal neuronal cell types can be found in the retina, including photoreceptors (the light sensitive cells in the retina), bipolar, horizontal, amacrine, and ganglion cells. A sixth type is that of interplexiform cells, that may be considered an amacrine cell variant. In addition, amacrine cells, that are usually localized to the inner nuclear layer, are also found in the ganglion cell layer, and these cells are called displaced amacrine cells (Figure 1). The flow of visual information goes from photoreceptors, through bipolar cells, to ganglion cells, which are the only output neurons and with their axons constitute the optic nerve, reaching the primary visual targets in the brain. Horizontal cells in the outer retina and amacrine cells in the inner retina provide horizontal modulation of this vertical pathway. The most heterogeneous retinal cell type is that of amacrine cells. Several different populations of amacrine cells can be distinguished, based on their neurochemical phenotypes, and a wide variety of neuroactive substances are expressed in the mammalian retina. In particular, several neuropeptides, together with their receptors, have been identified and investigated in mammalian retinas, and important information has been gathered about their physiological roles both in the adult and in the developing retina [1] as well as about their relevance in retinal disease [2]. Neuropeptides have been found to be principally expressed by populations of sparsely distributed, mostly GABAergic amacrine cells and by some ganglion cells. In contrast, neuropeptide receptors are expressed by variegated retinal cell populations, suggesting that peptidergic signaling participates in multiple circuits of visual information processing.

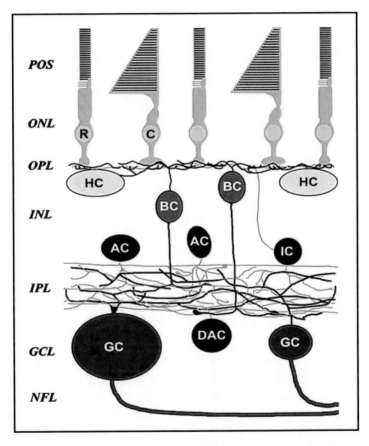

Figure 1. Schematic view of the mammalian retina showing all the principal neuronal cell types. *Abbreviations*: BC, bipolar cell; C, cone; DAC, displaced amacrine cell; GC, ganglion cell; GCL, ganglion cell layer; HC, horizontal cell; IC, interplexiform cell; INL, inner nuclear layer IPL, inner plexiform layer; NFL, nerve fiber layer; ONL, outer nuclear layer; OPL, outer plexiform layer; POS, photoreceptor outer segments; R, rod.

Among neuropeptides, somatostatin, or somatotropin release inhibiting factor (SRIF), has been widely investigated in the retina. SRIF is the product of a single gene, which gives two bioactive molecules: SRIF-14 and SRIF-28 [3]. SRIF-28 is a congener of SRIF-14 extended at the N-terminus. SRIF-14 is virtually the only form expressed in the retina [4]. SRIF interacts with five heptahelical transmembrane G-protein coupled receptors, designated sst_1- sst_5 (with two sst_2 receptor isoforms, sst_{2A} and sst_{2B}, derived from alternative mRNA splicing), that are coupled to different transduction pathways [3].

A number of reviews have been published in recent years reporting the expression of SRIF, its receptors and the signaling mechanisms that are involved in the functions of SRIF within the retina [1, 5-10]. Some of them have also considered the potential role of SRIF in retinal disease as it emerges from both animal and clinical studies [2, 8-9, 11-14]. In its first part, this chapter summarizes the expression patterns and the functional roles of SRIF and of its receptors in the mammalian retina; then it reviews the literature regarding the potential beneficial actions exerted by SRIF and its analogs against retinal disease to end up with a view of the state of the art of this branch of retinal research.

SRIF AND ITS RECEPTORS IN THE MAMMALIAN RETINA

Expression of SRIF in the Mammalian Retina

SRIF immunoreactivity is generally localized to sparsely distributed amacrine and/or displaced amacrine cells and, in some instances, to a subset of ganglion cells. In particular, in the mouse [15], rat [16-17], guinea pig [18-19] and human [20] retina, SRIF-containing cell bodies are located in both the inner nuclear layer (amacrine cells) and the ganglion cell layer (displaced amacrine cells). In the mouse retina, the population of SRIF-containing amacrine cells is sparsely distributed to all retinal regions, while the population of displaced amacrine cells is confined to the ventral retina [15]. In the rabbit, cat and primate retina, SRIF immunolabeling is almost exclusively observed in displaced amacrine cells confined to ventral retinal regions [21-27]. A few ganglion cells displaying SRIF immunoreactivity have been reported in the retina of the new world monkey *Tupaia belangeri* [22] and of the cat, where these cells have been found to be mostly localized to the inferior retina [28]. Finally, a transient population of SRIF containing ganglion cells has been discovered in the rat retina during postnatal development [29-30]. In spite of the very sparse distribution and in some cases of the segregation to specific retinal regions of SRIF-immunolabeled somata, SRIF-containing processes arborize extensively in the inner plexiform layer forming a continuous network in all retinal regions.

Expression of SRIF Receptors

The localization of SRIF receptors has been investigated using immunohistochemical approaches, and the data show that these receptors are expressed by a variety of retinal cell populations. In particular, in rat, rabbit and mouse retinas, sst_1 is predominantly expressed by SRIF containing amacrine cells [31-33], while in the rabbit retina, it is also found on the dopaminergic amacrine cells [32]. Of the two sst_2 isoforms, sst_{2A} has been localized in rat, rabbit and mouse retinas, where slightly different expression patterns have been reported. In summary, sst_{2A} is characteristically expressed by rod bipolar cells and by dopaminergic amacrine cells [15, 33-37]. The sst_{2B} isoform in the rat retina is predominantly found on the membrane of photoreceptors, indicating SRIF actions in the outer retina [34]. In the human retina, both sst_1 and sst_{2A} have been immunohistochemically localized throughout all retinal layers [38-39] and in endothelial cells of retinal blood vessels [38]. Regarding sst_4, it has been identified in ganglion cells of mouse and rat retinas [15, 40]. Finally, sst_5 has been reported in horizontal cells, in cholinergic and dopaminergic amacrine cells and in putative ganglion cells of rat and mouse retinas [41-42]. Immunohistochemical data concerning the retinal localization of sst_3 are not available, however, sst_3 mRNA has been detected in rat [43], mouse [15], and human [38-39] retinas.

Using retinas of mice in which sst_1 or sst_2 genes are genetically deleted [31, 44], important compensatory phenomena have been described. In particular, although changes in SRIF mRNA expression have not been reported in these knock-out (KO) retinas, the content of SRIF peptide is increased after sst_1 loss, whereas it is decreased in the case of sst_2 deletion. In addition, sst_2 becomes over-expressed as a consequence of sst_1 deletion, whereas sst_1 is over-expressed in sst_2 KO retinas. SRIF binding sites in sst_1 KO retinas have a density similar to that of wild-type (WT) retinas, suggesting that the relative proportion of SRIF receptors does not change as a consequence of sst_1 deletion and indicates that the loss of sst_1 can be totally compensated by an increase in sst_2. Some compensatory mechanisms also occur at the level of SRIF receptors in the absence of SRIF. Indeed, deletion of the SRIF gene has been found to induce an upregulation of SRIF binding sites [45].

Signaling Mechanisms

SRIF has been reported to inhibit adenylyl cyclase activity in the sheep retina [46], however SRIF has also been observed to increase adenylyl cyclase activation in amacrine cells of the rat retina [47]. In the mouse retina, sst_2 inhibits adenylyl cyclase activity, probably through $G_{o\alpha}$-proteins [48], and sst_2 coupling to $G_{o\alpha}$-proteins has been also demonstrated in rabbit retina [49]. Interestingly, in the mouse retina, sst_1 inhibits adenylyl cyclase activity only after elimination of the sst_2 response, suggesting that there may be interactions between sst_1 and sst_2 when they signal via adenylyl cyclase [48]. In addition, the colocalization of sst_2 with NADPH diaphorase in rod bipolar cells and photoreceptors of both rat and rabbit retinas has been reported [34], suggesting a role of SRIF in the regulation of nitric oxide (NO) and intracellular cGMP levels, as confirmed by subsequent studies [6, 50-52] (see also paragraph *"Mechanisms mediating SRIF anti-ischemic effects"*). Conversely, activation of dopamine D1 receptors, and NO/peroxynitrite agents have been found to modulate SRIF release in the retina suggesting reciprocal interactions between SRIF, NO and dopamine [53]. Regarding the control of K^+ and Ca^{2+} conductances, SRIF, acting at sst_2, induces a prominent inhibition of large conductance, Ca^{2+}- and voltage-dependent K^+ channels as well as an inhibition of K^+-induced increase of the intracellular Ca^{2+} concentration ($[Ca^{2+}]i$) in rod bipolar cells isolated from the rabbit retina [54]. sst_2 negative coupling to K^+ conductances has been also demonstrated in rod bipolar cells isolated from the mouse retina [55]. In the same experimental model, sst_2 inhibits the K^+-induced increase of $[Ca^{2+}]i$ both in the cell body and in the axonal terminals [8]. Similarly, in the axonal terminals of rod bipolar cells isolated from the rat retina, SRIF strongly inhibits a K^+-induced increase of $[Ca^{2+}]i$ via L-type Ca^{2+} channels [56]. This effect of SRIF is likely to be mediated by sst_2 receptors. An effect of SRIF mediated by sst_4 has been recently reported on voltage gated ion channels in isolated rat ganglion cells. In this study, selective activation of sst_4 in isolated ganglion cells enhanced outward K^+ current and reduced inward Ca^{2+} current through L-type, but not N-type, Ca^{2+} channels [40].

Functional Roles of SRIF in the Retina

SRIF effects on mammalian retinal physiology were first reported as an influence of the peptide on the amplitude of the ERG b-wave in the rabbit retina *in vivo* [57]. Subsequently, it was observed that application of low concentrations of SRIF affects the amplitude of the a-, b- and c-waves in rabbit eyecup preparations. In addition, SRIF applications influenced the activity of different retinal cell types, such as bipolar, amacrine and ganglion cells and the horizontal cell network, demonstrating that SRIF actions are characterized by slow onset and long latency and providing the first account of the complexity of SRIF functional actions in the retina [58].

The localization of some of the SRIF receptors at locations that are distant from the sites of SRIF release in the inner plexiform layer suggests that this peptide may act in a paracrine fashion. In particular, SRIF functions are likely to result from the actions exerted by SRIF onto other neurotransmitter systems in the retina, including the release of SRIF itself. Indeed, SRIF may regulate its own release through sst_1, as indicated by the observation that sst_1 is expressed by all SRIF-containing amacrine cells and established by functional studies in rat retinal explants [7, 59]. Indirect evidence of the autoreceptor function of sst_1 is provided by studies in sst_1 or sst_2 KO mouse retinas. As mentioned above, the levels of SRIF peptide are increased in sst_1 KO retinas, while they are decreased in sst_2 KO retinas, suggesting that the amount of retinal SRIF is likely to depend on the expression levels of sst_1 [44]: in the absence of sst_1 (as in sst_1 KO retinas) inhibitory mechanisms limiting SRIF levels in the retina would be removed, while in the presence of sst_1 overexpression (as in sst_2 KO retinas) such mechanisms would be strengthened.

Based on the reported localization of SRIF receptors in dopaminergic amacrine cells, SRIF control of dopamine release has been postulated in mouse, rat and rabbit retinas. In effect, an influence of SRIF on retinal dopamine release has been observed in rat retinal explants, where the activation of either sst_1 or sst_2 has been found to cause an increase of dopamine release, while activation of sst_3 has no effect [60]. Since retinal levels of dopamine are known to be positively correlated with light intensity [61-62], this SRIF control of dopamine release is likely to have importance for the regulation of light adaptation.

SRIF has also been shown to participate in the control of glutamate release. Glutamate is the major excitatory neurotransmitter in the mammalian retina, and it is implicated in the neurotransmission along the pathway from photoreceptors to bipolar cells to ganglion cells. A common trait of the somatostatinergic system among different mammalian retinas is the expression of sst_{2A} in rod bipolar cells, which represent a major source of glutamate in the retina. This observation indicates that an important, conserved functional role of SRIF in the retina is the regulation of glutamate release mediated by sst_2 (discussed below).

There are some indications suggesting a possible participation of SRIF in the regulation of the retinal levels of GABA and acetylcholine. For instance, SRIF has been suggested to enhance GABAergic transmission through phosphorylation of $GABA_A$ receptors in amacrine cells of the rat retina [47]. This possibility is intriguing in view of the fine control that GABAergic amacrine cells exert on transmitter release from rod bipolar cell terminals through $GABA_C$ receptors [63]. If these GABAergic amacrine cells respond to a regulation by SRIF, this peptide would be able to control glutamate release by the rod bipolar cells through two distinct mechanisms: a direct action onto the sst_{2A} expressing rod bipolar cells, and an indirect action by regulating GABA release from amacrine cells. In addition, the fact that sst_5 immunoreactivity has been found in cholinergic amacrine cells of rat and mouse retinas [41-42], suggests that SRIF may be involved in the control of acetylcholine release, although earlier investigations showed that SRIF does not change the level of light-evoked release of acetylcholine from rabbit retina [57].

ANTI-ANGIOGENIC EFFECTS OF SRIF IN THE RETINA

SRIF Reduces Pro-angiogenic Factors and Neovascularization

Using a mouse model of oxygen-induced retinopathy, Smith and colleagues [64] reported that SRIF could reduce retinal neovascularization induced by oxygen shortage. In this model, newborn mice are exposed to high oxygen concentration, determining a hyperoxic condition in which retinal vessels become occluded due to lowered oxygen demand from retinal neurons. When the mice are returned to normoxic conditions, an ischemic state develops in the area of the occluded vessels, and new vessels are formed at the border of the ischemic area (neovascularization). The new vessels form characteristic tufts and invade the vitreous. Smith et al. [64] observed that the SRIF analog acting at sst_2, MK678, was able to reduce the retinal neovascularization in a process also including reduction of growth hormone levels and decrease of insulin-like growth factor-1 (IGF-1).

Many subsequent studies have investigated the potential role of SRIF analogs in counteracting the neovascular response that characterizes a debilitating retinal disease such as diabetic retinopathy (DR). This retinal pathology is a complication of diabetes mellitus and is the leading cause of blindness in working age people in industrialized countries. DR can be classified into two stages: nonproliferative and proliferative DR. The nonproliferative DR is characterized by microaneurysms and tiny hemorrhages, and usually it does not lead to visual impairments. Proliferative DR is characterized by the growth of new, aberrant blood vessels on the retinal surface. The new vessels are fragile and leaky, and they may cause vitreous hemorrhage followed by retinal detachment. Diabetic macular edema is also a result of diabetes and is characterized by increased vascular permeability and the deposition of hard exudates at the central retina. It is the principal cause of vision loss in diabetic patients with Type II diabetes [65-68].

SRIF levels in the vitreous of patients with DR are significantly lower than those in nondiabetic control subjects [69-70], suggesting that a deficit of SRIF may contribute to the process of retinal neovascularization and supports the concept that adequate levels of SRIF are needed for the maintenance of retinal homeostasis. Indeed, SRIF appears to be an important factor in the control of new vessel growth, and, as detailed below, SRIF analogs have been found to be effective in reducing retinal neovascularization both in animal models of retinal neovascularization and in patients with DR.

The process leading to the formation of new vessels in the diabetic retina is complex, however it may be simplified and regarded as the result of perturbations in the equilibrium between anti- and pro-angiogenic factors. For instance, a major pro-angiogenic factor is represented by IGF-1, which is stimulated by growth hormone and is increased in the vitreous of DR patients [70-71]. SRIF analogues are powerful inhibitors of growth hormone release and, therefore, they are also effective in reducing the blood concentration of IGF-1. Thus, the observed anti-angiogenic effects of SRIF in the retina may be mediated by SRIF inhibition of the growth hormone axis [72-74]. However, the role of circulating IGF-1 in the development of DR remains controversial [73, 75-76], and the effectiveness of SRIF analogues in reducing neovascularization in DR could also be due to an anti-angiogenic effect of these compounds in the retina through autocrine and paracrine effects, perhaps directly on retinal cells or on retinal blood vessels [72, 74, 77-80].

Indeed, it has been demonstrated that SRIF analogs are capable of influencing the levels of angiogenesis-associated factors that are expressed in the retina, such as IGF-1/IGF-1 receptors and vascular endothelial growth factor (VEGF)/VEGF receptors. In particular, in addition to circulating IGF-1, whose levels are regulated by the growth hormone, experimental studies have also demonstrated expression of IGF-1 and its receptors throughout the retina in vascular, neuronal and glial cells [73]. The levels of IGF-1 receptor mRNA are increased in the retinas of mouse models of both DR [81] and hypoxia-induced neovascularization [82], although conflicting results have been reported in rat retinas [83-85]. VEGF and its receptors are overexpressed in models of DR and in hypoxia/acidosis-induced proliferative retinopathy, causing increased vascular permeability and neovascularization [82-83, 86-91]. In a rat model of neovascularization, a time course of the expression of vascular growth associated factors has been performed, and SRIF levels appeared to be negatively correlated with those of VEGF [92].

SRIF Anti-angiogenic Actions Are Mediated by sst_2

The anti-angiogenic action of SRIF is likely to be mediated primarily by activation of sst_2. Indeed, in a study of hypoxic retinas of sst_1 or sst_2 KO mice, lack of sst_2, as in sst_2 KO retinas, was found to be associated with significantly higher levels of neovascularization. In contrast, enhanced SRIF function at sst_2, as in sst_1 KO retinas [55], limited the hypoxia-induced increase of VEGF, whereas sst_2 loss upregulated this increase. In addition, the expression of angiopoietin-1/2 and their receptors, which have different roles in the angiogenic process, was dysregulated in the absence of sst_2 [82]. Similar results were obtained using subcutaneous administrations of octreotide, (a long-lasting sst_2 preferred agonist) or cyanamid (a sst_2 antagonist) in both wild type and sst_1 or sst_2 KO mice with oxygen induced retinopathy. The neovascularization that is typically seen in this model was reduced by octreotide, whereas it was increased by cyanamid. In addition, no effects of octreotide or cyanamid on retinal neovascularization were observed in sst_2 KO retinas. Regarding VEGF, the hypoxia-induced increase in VEGF and its receptors was limited by octreotide and increased by cyanamid, and these effects were more pronounced in the presence of sst_2 overexpression, as in sst_1 KO retinas [93].

Other studies have also reported anti-angiogenic effects of sst_2 activation. A SRIF-camtothecin conjugate, a sst_2 directed compound, has a significant angioinhibitory effect on laser induced choroidal neovascularization in rats [94]. In addition, non peptide imidazolidin-2, 4-dione SRIF receptor agonists with sst_2/ sst_3 selectivity displayed anti-angiogenic activity in mouse models of retinal neovascularization or of choroidal neovascularization [95], while a novel sst_2 specific agonist (derived from 2-quinolones) inhibited ocular neovascularization in the rat laser-induced choroidal neovascularization model [96]. The anti-angiogenic effects of SRIF mediated by sst_2 may include the involvement of the protein kinase CK2 (formerly casein kinase 2), an ubiquitous serine/threonine protein kinase that is involved in a wide variety of biological processes, including retinal angiogenesis and pathogenesis of diabetic and other proliferative retinal microangiopathies [97].

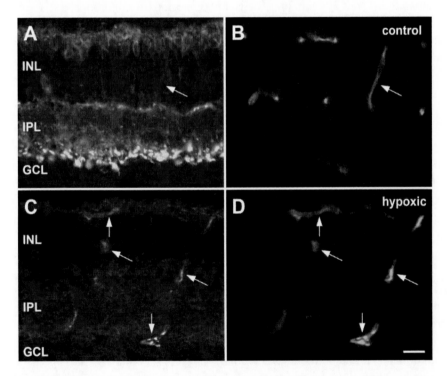

Figure 2. Double immunolabeled retinal sections using antibodies directed to sst_{2A} (A and C) in conjunction with antibodies directed to CD31, a marker of endothelial cells (B and D). In control retinas (A and B), sst_{2A} is localized to retinal neurons (specifically to rod bipolar cells and a subset of amacrine cells) and some retinal vessel results only faintly immunolabeled (arrow in A and B). In contrast, in hypoxic retinas (C and D), sst_{2A} immunolabeling is drastically decreased in neurons and it is mainly confined to retinal vessels (double-labeled vessels are indicated by arrows in C and D). See figure 1 for abbreviations. Scale bar: 20 μm.

A crosstalk between sst_2 and the CK2 pathway has been suggested on the basis that octreotide, combined with CK2 inhibitors, blocks retinal neovascularization in a mouse model of oxygen-induced retinopathy more efficiently than either compound alone [98-99].

Localization studies illustrating the immunostaining patterns of the isoform sst_{2A} of sst_2 demonstrated that hypoxia induces a drastic reduction of sst_{2A} in retinal neuronal cells and processes, while a relatively abundant sst_{2A} immunoreactivity becomes visible at the level of endothelial cells (Figure 2), suggesting that the hypoxic condition induces a delocalization of sst_{2A} which would mediate SRIF effects directly on retinal vessels [100]. Further studies employing triple label immunohistochemistry showed that if sst_{2A} is not expressed by VEGF-containing cells under normoxic conditions, sst_{2A} and VEGF co-localize in endothelial cells of retinal vessels when the retina is subjected to hypoxia [101]. These observations suggest that octreotide can prevent hypoxia-induced VEGF upregulation acting directly on VEGF-expressing endothelial cells and imply that sst_{2A} expressed by retinal vessels can receive an angioinhibitory action from sst_2 agonists. In addition, these results exclude any possible direct effect of octreotide on VEGF-containing cells under normoxia.

That a hypoxia-induced upregulation of sst_{2A} expression in the growing endothelium could permit the angioinhibitory action of SRIF analogs with high affinity for sst_2 is also supported by other *in vitro* and *in vivo* experimental findings. Indeed, quiescent human vascular endothelial cells do not express sst_2, but this receptor is expressed when the endothelial cells begin to grow [102-103]. In addition, studies in human eyes with choroidal neovascularization report that newly formed endothelial cells strongly express sst_2 [104], and the pattern of sst_2 expression in patients with diabetic retinopathy indicates that beneficial effects of sst_2 agonists may depend on the presence of sst_2 on newly formed vessels [39]. sst_2 receptors (mRNA and protein) have also been reported in bovine retinal endothelial cells, whose growth factor-induced proliferation under hypoxia results prevented by octreotide [77], and octreotide, as well as other non-peptide $sst_2/$ sst_3 agonists, has been observed to exert a direct inhibitory effect on growth factor-induced proliferation and migration of human retinal endothelial cells [95, 105].

Although the studies of SRIF inhibition of retinal neovascularization indicate sst_2 as the primary sst involved in such action, there is also some indication of possible synergism between different ssts and the involvement of sst_1 and sst_3. Indeed, sst_1 has been reported in blood vessels of rat inner retina [50], and administration of the sst_1 agonists BIM-23745 or BIM-23926 has been found to result in inhibition of human endothelial cell proliferation, migration, and sprouting in an extracellular matrix, while the same sst_1 agonists could limit VEGF expression *in vitro* [106]. Regarding sst_3, activation of this receptor has been shown to exert a direct inhibitory effect on the survival of human retinal endothelial cells [107]. In addition, experiments employing endothelial cell lines expressing sst_3 alone or a combination of ssts indicate that sst_3-mediated inhibition of eNOS and MAPK cascades is crucial for the antiproliferative effects of SRIF and that inhibition of endothelial cell proliferation may require a synergism between different ssts [108]. Although this experimental evidence suggests a role for sst_1 and/or sst_3 in mediating the retinal antiangiogenic actions of SRIF, further work employing sst_1 and sst_3 selective agonists is necessary to confirm the possible involvement of these receptors.

Signal Transduction Mechanisms Mediating Anti-angiogenic Effects of SRIF

Although each sst can influence different signal transduction pathways, all five receptors are functionally coupled to adenylyl cyclase (AC) inhibition [3] leading to a reduction of intracellular cAMP. Among mammalian retinas, an inhibition of AC activity by SRIF has been described in the mouse retina [48]. The possible involvement of the AC/cAMP pathway in mediating both hypoxia-induced retinal neoangiogenesis and SRIF protective actions has been studied in a model of oxygen- induced retinopathy using retinas of sst_1 and sst_2 KO mice (as noted above, sst_1 KO is a model of sst_2 over-expression and over-activation; sst_2 KO is a model of null sst_2 expression). The data showed that hypoxia increases AC responsiveness in wild type retinas and in retinas with null sst_2 expression, but not in sst_2 over-expressing retinas. In addition, the expression of the different AC isoforms was altered by the hypoxic treatment, with different patterns depending on sst_2 expression level. In particular, in hypoxia the expression of the AC VII isoform was enhanced in wild type retinas and it was further increased in retinas with null sst_2 expression, while it was decreased in sst_2 over-expressing retinas [109]. Together, these data suggest an involvement of AC/cAMP, and in particular of the AC VII isoform, in mediating both hypoxia-evoked retinal neoangiogenesis and SRIF protective actions.

The transcription factor hypoxia-inducible factor-1 (HIF-1) and its target genes, particularly VEGF, play a central role in retinal pathologies characterized by neovascularization [110]. In addition, as observed in a mouse model of oxygen induced retinopathy, overexpression of retinal VEGF is accompanied by up-regulation of the transcription factor STAT3 [100] and its phosphorylated form, pSTAT3 [100, 111]. In tumor cells, STAT3 regulates VEGF expression through modulation of HIF-1α, the regulatory subunit of HIF-1 [112-114], suggesting that interactions between STAT3 and HIF-1 may also regulate VEGF accumulation in response to hypoxia in the retina. On the other hand, octreotide not only prevents hypoxia-induced VEGF up-regulation [93], but also inhibits the increase of both STAT3 and pSTAT3 [100], suggesting that in the hypoxic retina octreotide may inhibit VEGF accumulation by influencing HIF-1α similar to findings in murine endocrine tumor cells [115].

These hypotheses have been examined in a recent paper using both pharmacological approaches and siRNA in mouse retinal explants cultured in normoxia or hypoxia [101]. The data revealed the existence of reciprocal interactions between STAT3 and HIF-1, which were observed to synergistically induce VEGF expression. In addition, treatment of hypoxic explants with pharmacological inhibitors of STAT3 or HIF-1 and administration of pharmacological activators of STAT3 or HIF-1 to normoxic explants to mimic a hypoxia-like response showed that octreotide prevents hypoxia-induced activation of STAT3 and HIF-1 and, consequently, the downstream increase in VEGF expression. The effect of octreotide on STAT3 activation is in part indirect, and it involves the blockade of VEGF receptor-2 (VEGFR-2) phosphorylation. The effect of octreotide on STAT3, HIF-1, VEGFR-2, and VEGF required Src homology region 2 domain-containing phosphatase 1 (SHP-1), which has been previously associated with the anti-proliferative effect of octreotide in tumor cells [116] and is known to negatively regulate VEGFR-2 [117-119]. In hypoxic retinal extracts, octreotide induced SHP-1 phosphorylation and activation, and inhibition of SHP-1 abolished the octreotide effect on STAT3, HIF-1, VEGFR-2, and VEGF [101]. Together, these data clarify the mechanism by which octreotide prevents hypoxia-induced VEGF up-regulation and demonstrate that sst_2 stimulation leads to the activation of SHP-1 that inhibits hypoxic levels of pSTAT3 and HIF-1α, thus preventing hypoxia-induced VEGF up-regulation. The effect of SHP-1 on pSTAT3 is, at least in part, mediated by the action of SHP-1 on VEGFR-2, which is activated concomitantly with up-regulation of VEGF release and which is in part responsible for STAT3 phosphorylation.

Clinical Evidence of the Effects of SRIF Analogs in DR and in Diabetic Macula Edema

SRIF analogs have been tested in clinical studies to assess their efficacy in preventing the progression of neovascularization in DR and diabetes-induced vascular damages leading to macular edema. The first studies reported an improvement of retinopathy in two out of six patients after prolonged administration of octreotide, with some effect on the levels of growth hormone [120]. In contrast, no significant effects of octreotide were reported on early retinopathy in type I (insulin-dependent) diabetes [121], but daily administration of octreotide for six months were shown to reduce the plasma levels of thromobomodulin, a marker of endothelial cell damage, in patients with type I diabetes [122]. Continuous infusion of the SRIF analog lanreotide (a sst_{2-5} preferring agonist) by subcutaneous pumps induced an improvement on the angiographic assessment in two out of eight patients with proliferative DR and had an indirect inhibitory effect on growth hormone [123]. In addition, long-term treatment with octreotide was reported to result in stabilization of neovascularization in patients suffering from proliferative DR progressing despite panretinal photocoagulation [124]. More recently, subcutaneous administrations of octreotide have been reported to retard the progression of advanced DR and to delay the time to laser surgery in patients with severe nonproliferative and early proliferative DR [125]. Octreotide has been also observed to reduce vitreous hemorrhage and loss of visual acuity in patients with high-risk proliferative DR after full scatter laser coagulation [126].

Effects of SRIF analogs have also been reported in the treatment of macular edema. Subcutaneous administrations of lanreotide in two patients with diffuse diabetic macular edema produced an improvement of the edema, but no significant effects on visual acuity [127]. In one patient with cystoid diabetic macular edema, octreotide (intramuscular, 1 injection/month for 1 year) had positive effects on visual acuity and induced a significant reduction of the cystoid changes in both eyes. In addition, the intraocular pressure had declined and no other complications were found [128]. In 14 patients with refractory postsurgical cystoid macular edema, octreotide (intramuscular, 1 injection/month for 6 months) appeared to improve retinal thickening, angiographic leakage, and visual acuity although the changes did not reach statistical significance [129]. Finally, in seven out of eight eyes of patients with dominant cystoid macular degeneration, an autosomal dominant trait of cystoid diabetic macular edema with poor visual prognosis, octreotide (intramuscular, 1 injection/month for 1 year) induced improvement of angiographic leakage and stabilization of visual acuity [130].

PROTECTIVE EFFECTS OF SRIF AGAINST HYPOXIA-INDUCED RETINAL NEURODEGENERATION

DR has been classically considered to be a microcirculatory disease of the retina. However, there is growing evidence suggesting that DR is a neurodegenerative disease of the eye, with signs of neurodegeneration being already present before any microcirculatory abnormalities can be detected [131-133]. In addition to apoptosis of retinal neuronal cells, another feature of retinal neurodegeneration is glial activation [134-135]. Both apoptosis and glial activation have been observed in the retina of diabetic patients before microvascular abnormalities and functional deficits [136-137].

A significant decrease of SRIF levels has been reported as an early event in DR. Probably, the neuronal damage that occurs in DR might be the cause of the downregulation of SRIF in DR patients. The lower expression of SRIF in the retina and retinal pigment epithelium is associated with a dramatic decrease of intravitreal SRIF levels in both DR [136] and diabetic macular edema [138]. Consequently, the SRIF actions against both neovascularization and fluid accumulation within the retina would be limited and the development of DR and diabetic macular edema would be favored.

Consistent with the signs of neurodegeneration observed both in patients with DR and in animal models of DR [132-133], in a recent study increases of caspase-3 activity and of the Bax/Bcl-2 ratio have been reported in mouse retinal explants maintained in hypoxic conditions. These hypoxia-induced increases of apoptotic signals were inhibited by octreotide in both wild type and sst_2 over-expressing retinas, indicating that sst_2 activation exerts a protective effect against retinal neuronal cell death induced by oxygen shortage. This reduced neuronal apoptosis results in improvement of the retinal functional activity. Indeed, in the same study, using the *in vivo* model of oxygen-induced retinopathy, a- and b-waves of the electroretinogram were observed to be drastically reduced by hypoxia, however both a- and b-waves were recovered by subcutaneous administrations of octreotide in both wild type and sst_2 over-expressing retinas. Neither the Bax/Bcl-2 ratio nor the electroretinographic responses were affected by octreotide in sst_2 KO mice [139].

PROTECTIVE EFFECTS OF SRIF AGAINST EXCITOTOXIC NEURONAL DEATH IN THE RETINA

A number of studies indicate that an ischemic condition is a major cause of neuronal loss in many retinal diseases, including DR. During ischemia, the concentration of glutamate increases in the retina, and there is evidence that glutamate excitotoxicity is a primary component of the damage produced in the retina by ischemia [131, 140-142]. SRIF analogs have been reported to exert potent anti-ischemic effects (reviewed in the next paragraph) mediated, at least in part, by inhibition of glutamate release. Some studies, however, have described protective effects of SRIF or SRIF agonists against excessive glutamate release or excitotoxic cell death in the retina independent of an ischemic context.

In mouse retinal explants, both SRIF and octreotide similarly reduced the evoked release of glutamate without affecting its basal level. This effect was not observed in sst_2 KO retinas [143], but it was larger in sst_2 over-expressing than in wild type retinas [55], confirming that inhibition of glutamate release was mediated by sst_2 activation. Unexpectedly, cyanamide, known as a sst_2 antagonist, also reduced the evoked glutamate release and this effect was no longer observed in sst_2 KO retinas, indicating that, with respect to the modulation of glutamate release, cyanamide may act as a sst_2 agonist [143]. In a different study, intraocular administrations of SRIF or of different sst_2 agonists (lanreotide or L-779976) have been found to protect the rat retina from neuronal loss caused by AMPA-induced neurotoxicity, while agonists of sst_1 or sst_4 had no effect [144]. Together, these data indicate that sst_2 is the main SRIF receptor mediating SRIF anti-excitotoxic effects, although a recent paper also suggests a role for sst_5. Indeed, intraocularly administered L-817,818, a sst_5 preferring agonist, effectively protected the rat retina from AMPA-induced neurotoxicity [145].

ANTI-ISCHEMIC EFFECTS OF SRIF IN THE RETINA

Ischemic Retina

Ischemia can be defined as inadequate blood supply to a local area due to impairment of the blood vessels in that area. Ischemia may also mean that blood flow is blocked, or that oxygen saturation in the blood flowing to the area is extremely low. An ischemic state often results in the shutdown of the area or in significant damage to the area. Both oxygen and glucose delivery are impaired during ischemia and toxic metabolites cannot be removed.

Ischemia should be distinguished from anoxia (a complete lack of oxygen) or hypoxia (a reduction in oxygen) [2, 12, 140]. Hypoxia means a reduction of oxygen availability or utilization, and it may develop as a consequence of reduced oxygen supply, reduced ambient pO_2, low hemoglobin or reduced tissue utilization caused by impairments in the mitochondrial cytochrome enzymes. In contrast, ischemia consists in a reduction of blood supply leading not only to decreased oxygen supply, but also to decreased nutrient delivery and limited or no removal of damaging cellular metabolites. Ischemia usually coexists with hypoxia. Ischemia always has a component of hypoxia/anoxia, but hypoxia/anoxia does not imply ischemia.

Retinal ischemia is a common clinical entity and, due to relatively ineffective treatment, remains a common cause of visual impairment and blindness [140, 146-147]. Indeed, ischemia in the retina and optic nerve is assumed to be involved in the pathogenesis of major vision-threatening diseases, such as age-related macular degeneration, DR and glaucoma. However, despite evidence from a substantial number of clinical and experimental studies, the role of retinal ischemia in these diseases is not understood in detail [148]. It should be noted that the cause of the symptoms in various retinal ischemic diseases is a mixture of hypoxia/anoxia rather than complete ischemia suggesting that hypoxia occurs in all "retinal ischemic diseases" [149].

Generally, ischemia leads to impaired homeostatic responses which, in turn, provoke tissue injury due to cell loss by apoptosis [140, 146, 149]. Ischemia is a primary cause of neuronal death in the retina, and it can be considered as a sort of final common pathway in retinal diseases leading to irreversible morphological damage and vision loss. As reviewed previously [2, 12, 140], although transient loss of both glucose and oxygen is not immediately lethal, the prolonged deprivation of these substrates leads to depletion of ATP stores and to retinal damage. The death of retinal neurons is the final outcome deriving from an extremely complex cascade of biochemical responses initiated by energy failure. The main factors involved in ischemia-induced retinal degeneration are thought to be excitatory neurotransmitter release (i.e., glutamate), glial dysfunction, Ca^{2+} overload, formation of reactive oxygen species and free radicals (oxidative stress), and release of potentially toxic mediators by activated inflammatory cells. These events finally lead to death (mostly by apoptosis) of certain cell populations or the entire retina depending on the strength and duration of the ischemic event.

Of importance, ischemia is also the driving force for the formation of new vessels in the retina. As mentioned above, aberrant retinal neovascularization is a major cause of visual impairment and it is observed in ischemic retinopathies such as proliferative DR, retinopathy of prematurity, central vein occlusion and branch retinal vein occlusion [150].

Evidence of Anti-ischemic Effects of SRIF Mediated by sst_2

There is wide experimental evidence that SRIF or its analogues, mainly acting at sst_2, may exert potent protective effects against ischemia. The first observations of possible anti-ischemic actions of SRIF were reported in guinea pig retinas, where octreotide was observed to protect against ischemia reperfusion injury [151]. Subsequently, using an ex vivo NaCN/iodoacetic acid chemical model of rat retinal ischemia, sst_2 activation was shown to reverse the ischemia-induced decrease of different retinal cell populations and to decrease the number of apoptotic cells visualized with the TUNEL assay [152]. These observations have been implemented using an ex vivo model of chemical ischemia (hypoxia/iodoacetic acid) of the mouse retina and retinas of sst_1 KO or sst_2 KO animals [153]. In these studies, sst_1 KO retinas, where sst_2 are over-expressed and over-functional, displayed a marked reduction of cell death with respect to wild type or sst_2 KO retinas. In addition, the expression of protease caspase-3mRNA, a marker of apoptotic cell death, was also reduced in sst_1 KO as compared to wild type retinas. Using the same model of the ex vivo ischemic mouse retina, it was shown that the use of SRIF or of sst agonists, such as the multireceptor ligand pasireotide or the sst_2 agonist octreotide, are effective in reducing the number of apoptotic neurons and the expression of apoptotic markers, such as caspase-3 mRNA. In contrast, cell death was significantly increased after blocking sst_2 receptors with the sst_2 receptor antagonist cyanamide [154]. Taken together, these observations demonstrate that an increased presence/activation of functional sst_2 protects against neuronal death caused by retinal ischemia (Figure 3).

Immunohistochemical analyses have identified some of the retinal cell populations that are protected by sst_2 activation in ischemic retinas. In particular, in explants of the rat retina subjected to chemical ischemia, sst_2 agonists prevented, at least in part, the loss of several retinal cell populations, including choline acetyltransferase-, tyrosine hydroxylase-, nitric oxide synthase-immunoreactive amacrine cells as well as the rod bipolar cells [152]. On the other hand, other studies in ex vivo ischemic mouse retinas have demonstrated that the extent of sst_2-mediated protection may vary among different retinal cell populations, suggesting a high level of complexity within the neuroprotective mechanisms of sst_2. For instance, the population of rod bipolar cells, which express sst_2 at high levels, is severely affected by ischemia, but it is significantly spared in the presence of sst_2 overexpression, as in sst_1 KO retinas, while it is more heavily damaged in the absence of sst_2, as in sst_2 KO retinas [153].

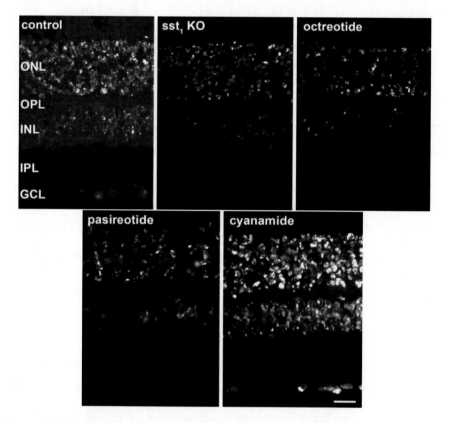

Figure 3. TUNEL staining in retinal sections from ex vivo ischemic (hypoxia/iodoacetic acid) mouse retinas. In wild type, untreated retinas (control), many apoptotic cells are labeled in the ONL, the INL and the GCL. The number of apoptotic cells is dramatically decreased in sst_1 KO retinas. Similarly, less dying cells are seen in the wild type retina treated with 10^{-5}M octreotide or pasireotide. In contrast, treatment with the sst_2 antagonist cyanamide (10^{-5}M) results in increased TUNEL labeling in all the retinal nuclear layers. See figure 1 for abbreviations. Scale bar: 20 μm.

Using the retina of sst_1 KO mice, characterized by over-expression of functional sst_2 [8, 31, 48, 55], it was expected that sst_2 agonist administration resulted in increased protection from ischemic damage, however, in contrast to this expectation, a potentiation of the ischemic damage was observed. This apparent contradiction has been clarified by experimental data at pharmacological and molecular level showing that over-expressed sst_2 are likely to be rapidly desensitized by agonists, thus resulting in a decrease of their functional activity [154].

Mechanisms Mediating SRIF Anti-ischemic Effects

As mentioned above, SRIF analogs may limit the extent of neuronal damage caused by ischemia inducing a reduction of the glutamate release and of the excitotoxic insult that is typically found in ischemic conditions. In ischemic ex vivo mouse retinas, retinal glutamate release was observed to increase under ischemia, but this increase was significantly reduced in sst_1 KO retinas [153]. These observations have been confirmed in the same model using the SRIF analogs pasireotide and octreotide, which turned out to be effective in reducing excessive glutamate release in ischemic retinas [154]. The inhibiting action of sst_2 on excitatory aminoacid release in the ischemic retina is further substantiated by studies using the ex vivo rat retinal ischemia model, where the ischemia-induced [^{3}H] D-aspartate release was significantly decreased by administration of octreotide, while it was increased after administration of the sst_2 antagonist cyanamide [155]. Together, these data indicate that sst_2 receptor activation results in inhibition of excessive glutamate release caused by ischemia and has an anti-excitotoxic effect in the ischemic retina.

Activation of ionotropic glutamate receptors caused by excessive glutamate release triggers a subsequent cascade of events involving the increase of intracellular calcium, which would promote cell death [140]. As mentioned above, sst_2 activation inhibits K^+-induced increase of the intracellular calcium in isolated retinal rod bipolar cells [54]. In addition, SRIF has been found to inhibit neuronal calcium currents, in chick ciliary ganglion neurons, via a cyclic GMP (cGMP) -dependent mechanism [156]. As in other systems, also in retina NO activates a soluble guanylyl cyclase leading to an increase in cGMP production [157-158]. Therefore, a sst_2-mediated regulation of NO and cGMP has been proposed as a mechanism mediating the anti-ischemic effects of sst_2 activation [52].

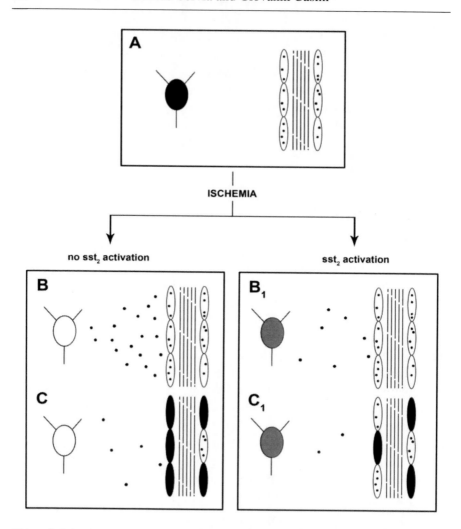

Figure 4. Schematic view of the VEGF response in ischemic mouse retinas either in the absence or in the presence of sst_2 activation. In non ischemic retinas, VEGF (indicated by dark staining in the neuron and by dark dots in the endothelial cells) is mainly in neuronal cells and scarcely in vessels (A). Ischemia in the absence of sst_2 activation induces a massive release of VEGF from damaged neurons (B) and the released VEGF is then taken up by endothelial cells (C). In contrast, in the presence of sst_2 activation, neurons are protected from the ischemic insult and release less VEGF (B_1). Therefore, less VEGF is taken up by endothelial cells (C_1).

In rat retinal explants, SRIF has been shown to increase cGMP levels via a SRIF/ sst_2/NO mechanism [159], and both NO and cGMP have been found to be implicated in the anti-ischemic action promoted by sst_2 activation. Indeed,

NO donors or a membrane permeable cGMP analogue protected ex vivo rat retina ischemic preparations from cell death evaluated with immuno-histochemistry and TUNEL labeling. In addition, NO synthase or guanylyl cyclase inhibitors reversed the protective effect of the sst_{2-5} preferring SRIF analogue lanreotide, but a sst_5 antagonist had no effect on NO release [52]. Together, these data indicate that sst_2 anti-ischemic actions based on the reduction of the excitotoxic effect are likely to be mediated by an intracellular cascade involving NO activation and cGMP production.

The production of reactive oxygen species and an increase of oxidative stress in the retina are among the effects triggered by ischemia and leading to cell death [140]. Some data have been produced indicating that activation of sst_2 may influence the oxidative state in the retina favoring the decrease of oxidative stress caused by ischemia. Indeed, octreotide has been reported to reduce the increase of lipid peroxidation levels observed subsequent to ischemia/reperfusion in guinea pig retinas [151]. In addition, in recent experiments using a new model of chemical ischemia (hypoxia/10^{-3}M sodium azide) in ex vivo mouse retinas, a notable decrease of reduced glutathione (GSH) accompanied by a significant increase of oxidized glutathione (GSSG) was observed when ischemic retinas were treated with 10^{-5}M octreotide (D. Cervia and G. Casini, unpublished observation). A measurement of the ratio of GSH to GSSG is a useful indicator of oxidative stress. When cells are exposed to increased levels of oxidative stress, GSSG will accumulate and the ratio of GSH to GSSG will decrease. These data show that sst_2 activation results in a major inhibition of oxidative stress in the ischemic retina.

A further effect of sst_2 activation in the ischemic retina has been recently reported in ex vivo ischemic (hypoxia/iodoacetic acid for 1 hour) mouse retinas [160]. Since an ischemic condition not only causes cell death but also induces a vascular response, possible changes in VEGF expression, release or distribution patterns in the ischemic retina were assessed and the effects of sst_2 activation on VEGF were investigated using sst_1 KO mice or administration of SRIF or octreotide. The results of these studies showed that ischemia in wild type retinas results in increased VEGF release and decreased VEGF mRNA expression, indicating that during acute ischemia the retina releases VEGF but is incapable of DNA transcription, and that both effects are inhibited by SRIF or octreotide. In addition, VEGF immunoreactivity was observed in retinal neurons and scarcely in vessels, but ischemia caused a significant shift of VEGF localization from neurons to endothelial cells of retinal vessels. This increase of VEGF immunoreactivity in retinal vessels was reduced in sst_2 over-expressing, sst_1 KO retinas and in wild type retinas treated with SRIF or octreotide. A VEGF trap also limited this increase in ischemic retinas, demonstrating that VEGF observed in endothelial cells was of extracellular origin. Together, these data indicate a VEGF response to acute ischemia, in which neurons, severely damaged by ischemia, drastically reduce gene expression (including VEGF expression) and release all of their VEGF content.

Then, the VEGF massively released by the dying neurons reaches the retinal capillaries where it is likely to initiate the mechanisms for the formation of new vessels. The activation of sst_2 protects neurons from apoptotic damage, thereby limiting VEGF release and the VEGF response (Figure 4).

CONCLUSION

In this chapter, the experimental data demonstrating strong anti-angiogenic and anti-ischemic effects of SRIF or SRIF analogs have been reviewed. From the overall analysis of these data, it appears that clinical strategies to treat retinal pathologies relaying on SRIF-based molecules may lead to important achievements.

On the other hand, it must be noted that the interest around the possible use of SRIF analogs to treat DR dates back to the early-mid eighties [161-163], when the goal was to inhibit growth hormone circulating levels. After about thirty years and several clinical studies (see paragraph "*Clinical evidence of the effects of SRIF analogs in DR and in diabetic macula edema*"), although some positive results have been collected, SRIF analogs seem to be still far from becoming the treatment of choice to resolve retinal pathologies such as DR.

This may be due to a number of reasons, but the central point is that, perhaps, only recently detailed information on the effects of SRIF analogs (mostly of those acting at sst_2) and on the transduction mechanisms they activate has been achieved. Indeed, in the last ten years notable advances have made in the knowledge of the multifaceted effects elicited by SRIF both in physiologic retinal functions and in models of retinal pathologies, and some light has been shed onto the intracellular molecules mediating these effects, allowing the idea of new strategies to treat retinal diseases based not only on the use of SRIF analogs but also on the manipulation of intracellular pathways.

REFERENCES

[1] Bagnoli, P.; Dal Monte, M. & Casini, G. (2003). Expression of neuropeptides and their receptors in the developing retina of mammals. *Histol Histopathol, 18,* 1219-1242.

[2] Cervia, D. & Casini, G. (2012). The neuropeptide systems and their potential role in the treatment of mammalian retinal ischemia: a developing story. *Curr Neuropharmacol, in press.*

[3] Cervia, D. & Bagnoli, P. (2007). An update on somatostatin receptor signaling in native systems and new insights on their pathophysiology. *Pharmacol Ther, 116,* 322-341.

[4] Patel, Y. C. (1999). Somatostatin and its receptor family. *Front Neuroendocrinol, 20,* 157-198.

[5] Thermos, K. (2003). Functional mapping of somatostatin receptors in the retina: a review. *Vision Res, 43,* 1805-1815.

[6] Thermos, K. (2008). Novel signals mediating the functions of somatostatin: the emerging role of NO/cGMP. *Mol Cell Endocrinol, 286,* 49-57.

[7] Thermos, K.; Bagnoli, P.; Epelbaum, J. & Hoyer, D. (2006). The somatostatin sst1 receptor: an autoreceptor for somatostatin in brain and retina? *Pharmacol Ther, 110,* 455-464.

[8] Casini, G.; Catalani, E.; Dal Monte, M. & Bagnoli, P. (2005). Functional aspects of the somatostatinergic system in the retina and the potential therapeutic role of somatostatin in retinal disease. *Histol Histopathol, 20,* 615-632.

[9] Cervia, D.; Casini, G. & Bagnoli, P. (2008). Physiology and pathology of somatostatin in the mammalian retina: a current view. *Mol Cell Endocrinol, 286,* 112-122.

[10] Johnson, J.; Rickman, D. W. & Brecha, N. C. (2000). Somatostatin and somatostatin subtype 2A expression in the mammalian retina. *Microsc Res Tech, 50,* 103-111.

[11] Grant, M. B. & Caballero, S. (2002). Somatostatin analogues as drug therapies for retinopathies. *Drugs Today (Barc), 38,* 783-791.

[12] Cervia, D. & Casini, G. (2012). Recent advances in cellular and molecular aspects of mammalian retinal ischemia. *World J Pharmacol, 1,* 30-43.

[13] Vasilaki, A. & Thermos, K. (2009). Somatostatin analogues as therapeutics in retinal disease. *Pharmacol Ther, 122,* 324-333.

[14] Palii, S. S.; Caballero, S., Jr.; Shapiro, G. & Grant, M. B. (2007). Medical treatment of diabetic retinopathy with somatostatin analogues. *Expert Opin Investig Drugs, 16,* 73-82.

[15] Cristiani, R.; Petrucci, C.; Dal Monte, M. & Bagnoli, P. (2002). Somatostatin (SRIF) and SRIF receptors in the mouse retina. *Brain Res, 936,* 1-14.

[16] Larsen, J. N.; Bersani, M.; Olcese, J.; Holst, J. J. & Moller, M. (1990). Somatostatin and prosomatostatin in the retina of the rat: an immunohistochemical, in-situ hybridization, and chromatographic study. *Vis Neurosci, 5,* 441-452.

[17] Sagar, S. M.; Marshall, P. E. & Landis, D. M. (1985). Immunoreactive somatostatin in the rat retina: light microscopic immunocytochemistry and chromatographic characterization. *Brain Res, 336,* 235-242.

[18] Spira, A. W.; Shimizu, Y. & Rorstad, O. P. (1984). Localization, chromatographic characterization, and development of somatostatin-like immunoreactivity in the guinea pig retina. *J Neurosci, 4,* 3069-3079.

[19] Tornqvist, K.; Uddman, R.; Sundler, F. & Ehinger, B. (1982). Somatostatin and VIP neurons in the retina of different species. *Histochemistry, 76,* 137-152.

[20] Tornqvist, K. & Ehinger, B. (1988). Peptide immunoreactive neurons in the human retina. *Invest Ophthalmol Vis Sci, 29,* 680-686.

[21] Mitrofanis, J.; Robinson, S. R. & Provis, J. M. (1989). Somatostatinergic neurones of the developing human and cat retinae. *Neurosci Lett, 104,* 209-216.

[22] Engelmann, R. & Peichl, L. (1996). Unique distribution of somatostatin-immunoreactive cells in the retina of the tree shrew (Tupaia belangeri). *Eur J Neurosci, 8,* 220-228.

[23] Rickman, D. W.; Blanks, J. C. & Brecha, N. C. (1996). Somatostatin-immunoreactive neurons in the adult rabbit retina. *J Comp Neurol, 365,* 491-503.

[24] White, C. A.; Chalupa, L. M.; Johnson, D. & Brecha, N. C. (1990). Somatostatin-immunoreactive cells in the adult cat retina. *J Comp Neurol, 293,* 134-150.

[25] Marshak, D. W. (1989). Peptidergic neurons of the macaque monkey retina. *Neurosci Res Suppl, 10,* S117-130.

[26] Sagar, S. M. & Marshall, P. E. (1988). Somatostatin-like immunoreactive material in associational ganglion cells of human retina. *Neuroscience, 27,* 507-516.

[27] Sagar, S. M. (1987). Somatostatin-like immunoreactive material in the rabbit retina: immunohistochemical staining using monoclonal antibodies. *J Comp Neurol, 266,* 291-299.

[28] White, C. A. & Chalupa, L. M. (1991). Subgroup of alpha ganglion cells in the adult cat retina is immunoreactive for somatostatin. *J Comp Neurol, 304,* 1-13.

[29] Xiang, Z.; Jiang, L. & Kang, Z. (2001). Transient expression of somatostatin mRNA in developing ganglion cell layers of rat retina. *Brain Res Dev Brain Res, 128,* 25-33.

[30] Fontanesi, G.; Casini, G.; Thanos, S. & Bagnoli, P. (1997). Transient somatostatin-immunoreactive ganglion cells in the developing rat retina. *Brain Res Dev Brain Res, 103,* 119-125.

[31] dal Monte, M.; Petrucci, C.; Vasilaki, A.; Cervia, D.; Grouselle, D.; Epelbaum, J.; Kreienkamp, H. J.; Richter, D.; Hoyer, D. & Bagnoli, P. (2003). Genetic deletion of somatostatin receptor 1 alters somatostatinergic transmission in the mouse retina. *Neuropharmacology, 45,* 1080-1092.

[32] Cristiani, R.; Fontanesi, G.; Casini, G.; Petrucci, C.; Viollet, C. & Bagnoli, P. (2000). Expression of somatostatin subtype 1 receptor in the rabbit retina. *Invest Ophthalmol Vis Sci, 41,* 3191-3199.

[33] Helboe, L. & Moller, M. (1999). Immunohistochemical localization of somatostatin receptor subtypes sst1 and sst2 in the rat retina. *Invest Ophthalmol Vis Sci, 40,* 2376-2382.

[34] Vasilaki, A.; Gardette, R.; Epelbaum, J. & Thermos, K. (2001). NADPH-diaphorase colocalization with somatostatin receptor subtypes sst2A and sst2B in the retina. *Invest Ophthalmol Vis Sci, 42,* 1600-1609.

[35] Fontanesi, G.; Gargini, C. & Bagnoli, P. (2000). Postnatal development of somatostatin 2A (sst2A) receptors expression in the rabbit retina. *Brain Res Dev Brain Res, 123,* 67-80.

[36] Johnson, J.; Wong, H.; Walsh, J. H. & Brecha, N. C. (1998). Expression of the somatostatin subtype 2A receptor in the rabbit retina. *J Comp Neurol, 393,* 93-101.

[37] Johnson, J.; Wu, V.; Wong, H.; Walsh, J. H. & Brecha, N. C. (1999). Somatostatin receptor subtype 2A expression in the rat retina. *Neuroscience, 94,* 675-683.

[38] Klisovic, D. D.; O'Dorisio, M. S.; Katz, S. E.; Sall, J. W.; Balster, D.; O'Dorisio, T. M.; Craig, E. & Lubow, M. (2001). Somatostatin receptor gene expression in human ocular tissues: RT-PCR and immunohistochemical study. *Invest Ophthalmol Vis Sci, 42,* 2193-2201.

[39] van Hagen, P. M.; Baarsma, G. S.; Mooy, C. M.; Ercoskan, E. M.; ter Averst, E.; Hofland, L. J.; Lamberts, S. W. & Kuijpers, R. W. (2000). Somatostatin and somatostatin receptors in retinal diseases. *Eur J Endocrinol, 143 Suppl 1,* S43-51.

[40] Farrell, S. R.; Raymond, I. D.; Foote, M.; Brecha, N. C. & Barnes, S. (2010). Modulation of voltage-gated ion channels in rat retinal ganglion cells mediated by somatostatin receptor subtype 4. *J Neurophysiol, 104,* 1347-1354.

[41] Ke, J. B. & Zhong, Y. M. (2007). Expression of somatostatin receptor subtype 5 in rat retinal amacrine cells. *Neuroscience, 144,* 1025-1032.

[42] Wu, X. H.; Deng, Q. Q.; Jiang, S. X.; Yang, X. L. & Zhong, Y. M. (2012). Distribution of somatostatin receptor 5 in mouse and bullfrog retinas. *Peptides, 33,* 291-297.

[43] Mori, M.; Aihara, M. & Shimizu, T. (1997). Differential expression of somatostatin receptors in the rat eye: SSTR4 is intensely expressed in the iris/ciliary body. *Neurosci Lett, 223,* 185-188.

[44] Casini, G.; Dal Monte, M.; Petrucci, C.; Gambellini, G.; Grouselle, D.; Allen, J. P.; Kreienkamp, H. J.; Richter, D.; Epelbaum, J. & Bagnoli, P. (2004). Altered morphology of rod bipolar cell axonal terminals in the retinas of mice carrying genetic deletion of somatostatin subtype receptor 1 or 2. *Eur J Neurosci, 19,* 43-54.

[45] Mastrodimou, N.; Vasilaki, A.; Papadioti, A.; Low, M. J.; Hoyer, D. & Thermos, K. (2006). Somatostatin receptors in wildtype and somatostatin deficient mice and their involvement in nitric oxide physiology in the retina. *Neuropeptides, 40,* 365-373.

[46] Colas, B.; Valencia, A. M.; Prieto, J. C. & Arilla, E. (1992). Somatostatin binding and modulation of adenylate cyclase in ovine retina membranes. *Mol Cell Endocrinol, 88,* 111-117.

[47] Feigenspan, A. & Bormann, J. (1994). Facilitation of GABAergic signaling in the retina by receptors stimulating adenylate cyclase. *Proc Natl Acad Sci U S A, 91,* 10893-10897.

[48] Pavan, B.; Fiorini, S.; Dal Monte, M.; Lunghi, L.; Biondi, C.; Bagnoli, P. & Cervia, D. (2004). Somatostatin coupling to adenylyl cyclase activity in the mouse retina. *Naunyn Schmiedebergs Arch Pharmacol, 370,* 91-98.

[49] Vasilaki, A.; Georgoussi, Z. & Thermos, K. (2003). Somatostatin receptors (sst2) are coupled to Go and modulate GTPase activity in the rabbit retina. *J Neurochem, 84,* 625-632.

[50] Vasilaki, A.; Mouratidou, M.; Schulz, S. & Thermos, K. (2002). Somatostatin mediates nitric oxide production by activating sst(2) receptors in the rat retina. *Neuropharmacology, 43,* 899-909.

[51] Vasilaki, A.; Papadaki, T.; Notas, G.; Kolios, G.; Mastrodimou, N.; Hoyer, D.; Tsilimbaris, M.; Kouroumalis, E.; Pallikaris, I. & Thermos, K. (2004). Effect of somatostatin on nitric oxide production in human retinal pigment epithelium cell cultures. *Invest Ophthalmol Vis Sci, 45,* 1499-1506.

[52] Mastrodimou, N.; Kiagiadaki, F. & Thermos, K. (2008). The role of nitric oxide and cGMP in somatostatin's protection against retinal ischemia. *Invest Ophthalmol Vis Sci, 49,* 342-349.

[53] Kiagiadaki, F.; Koulakis, E. & Thermos, K. (2008). Dopamine (D1) receptor activation and nitrinergic agents influence somatostatin levels in rat retina. *Exp Eye Res, 86,* 18-24.

[54] Petrucci, C.; Resta, V.; Fieni, F.; Bigiani, A. & Bagnoli, P. (2001). Modulation of potassium current and calcium influx by somatostatin in rod bipolar cells isolated from the rabbit retina via sst2 receptors. *Naunyn Schmiedebergs Arch Pharmacol, 363,* 680-694.

[55] Bigiani, A.; Petrucci, C.; Ghiaroni, V.; dal Monte, M.; Cozzi, A.; Kreienkamp, H. J.; Richter, D. & Bagnoli, P. (2004). Functional correlates of somatostatin receptor 2 overexpression in the retina of mice with genetic deletion of somatostatin receptor 1. *Brain Res, 1025,* 177-185.

[56] Johnson, J.; Caravelli, M. L. & Brecha, N. C. (2001). Somatostatin inhibits calcium influx into rat rod bipolar cell axonal terminals. *Vis Neurosci, 18,* 101-108.

[57] Cunningham, J. R. & Neal, M. J. (1983). Effect of gamma-aminobutyric acid agonists, glycine, taurine and neuropeptides on acetylcholine release from the rabbit retina. *J Physiol, 336,* 563-577.

[58] Zalutsky, R. A. & Miller, R. F. (1990). The physiology of somatostatin in the rabbit retina. *J Neurosci, 10,* 383-393.

[59] Mastrodimou, N. & Thermos, K. (2004). The somatostatin receptor (sst1) modulates the release of somatostatin in rat retina. *Neurosci Lett, 356,* 13-16.

[60] Kouvidi, E.; Papadopoulou-Daifoti, Z. & Thermos, K. (2006). Somatostatin modulates dopamine release in rat retina. *Neurosci Lett, 391,* 82-86.

[61] Boelen, M. K.; Boelen, M. G. & Marshak, D. W. (1998). Light-stimulated release of dopamine from the primate retina is blocked by 1-2-amino-4-phosphonobutyric acid (APB). *Vis Neurosci, 15,* 97-103.

[62] Djamgoz, M. B. & Wagner, H. J. (1992). Localization and function of dopamine in the adult vertebrate retina. *Neurochem Int, 20,* 139-191.

[63] Vaquero, C. F. & de la Villa, P. (1999). Localisation of the GABA(C) receptors at the axon terminal of the rod bipolar cells of the mouse retina. *Neurosci Res, 35,* 1-7.

[64] Smith, L. E.; Kopchick, J. J.; Chen, W.; Knapp, J.; Kinose, F.; Daley, D.; Foley, E.; Smith, R. G. & Schaeffer, J. M. (1997). Essential role of growth hormone in ischemia-induced retinal neovascularization. *Science, 276,* 1706-1709.

[65] Porta, M. & Allione, A. (2004). Current approaches and perspectives in the medical treatment of diabetic retinopathy. *Pharmacol Ther, 103,* 167-177.

[66] Pemp, B. & Schmetterer, L. (2008). Ocular blood flow in diabetes and age-related macular degeneration. *Can J Ophthalmol, 43,* 295-301.

[67] Ciulla, T. A.; Amador, A. G. & Zinman, B. (2003). Diabetic retinopathy and diabetic macular edema: pathophysiology, screening, and novel therapies. *Diabetes Care, 26,* 2653-2664.

[68] Aiello, L. P. (2008). Targeting intraocular neovascularization and edema--one drop at a time. *N Engl J Med, 359,* 967-969.

[69] Hernandez, C.; Carrasco, E.; Casamitjana, R.; Deulofeu, R.; Garcia-Arumi, J. & Simo, R. (2005). Somatostatin molecular variants in the vitreous fluid: a comparative study between diabetic patients with proliferative diabetic retinopathy and nondiabetic control subjects. *Diabetes Care, 28,* 1941-1947.

[70] Simo, R.; Lecube, A.; Sararols, L.; Garcia-Arumi, J.; Segura, R. M.; Casamitjana, R. & Hernandez, C. (2002). Deficit of somatostatin-like immunoreactivity in the vitreous fluid of diabetic patients: possible role in the development of proliferative diabetic retinopathy. *Diabetes Care, 25,* 2282-2286.

[71] DeBosch, B. J.; Baur, E.; Deo, B. K.; Hiraoka, M. & Kumagai, A. K. (2001). Effects of insulin-like growth factor-1 on retinal endothelial cell glucose transport and proliferation. *J Neurochem, 77,* 1157-1167.

[72] Boehm, B. O. (2007). Use of long-acting somatostatin analogue treatment in diabetic retinopathy. *Dev Ophthalmol, 39,* 111-121.

[73] Wilkinson-Berka, J. L.; Wraight, C. & Werther, G. (2006). The role of growth hormone, insulin-like growth factor and somatostatin in diabetic retinopathy. *Curr Med Chem, 13,* 3307-3317.

[74] Garcia de la Torre, N.; Wass, J. A. & Turner, H. E. (2002). Antiangiogenic effects of somatostatin analogues. *Clin Endocrinol (Oxf), 57,* 425-441.

[75] Janssen, J. A.; Jacobs, M. L.; Derkx, F. H.; Weber, R. F.; van der Lely, A. J. & Lamberts, S. W. (1997). Free and total insulin-like growth factor I (IGF-I), IGF-binding protein-1 (IGFBP-1), and IGFBP-3 and their relationships to the presence of diabetic retinopathy and glomerular hyperfiltration in insulin-dependent diabetes mellitus. *J Clin Endocrinol Metab, 82,* 2809-2815.

[76] Janssen, J. A. & Lamberts, S. W. (2000). Circulating IGF-I and its protective role in the pathogenesis of diabetic angiopathy. *Clin Endocrinol (Oxf), 52,* 1-9.

[77] Baldysiak-Figiel, A.; Lang, G. K.; Kampmeier, J. & Lang, G. E. (2004). Octreotide prevents growth factor-induced proliferation of bovine retinal endothelial cells under hypoxia. *J Endocrinol, 180,* 417-424.

[78] Dasgupta, P. (2004). Somatostatin analogues: multiple roles in cellular proliferation, neoplasia, and angiogenesis. *Pharmacol Ther, 102,* 61-85.

[79] Higgins, R. D.; Yan, Y. & Schrier, B. K. (2002). Somatostatin analogs inhibit neonatal retinal neovascularization. *Exp Eye Res, 74,* 553-559.

[80] Davis, M. I.; Wilson, S. H. & Grant, M. B. (2001). The therapeutic problem of proliferative diabetic retinopathy: targeting somatostatin receptors. *Horm Metab Res, 33,* 295-299.

[81] Kuang, H.; Zou, W.; Liu, D.; Shi, R.; Cheng, L.; Yin, H. & Liu, X. (2003). The potential role of IGF-I receptor mRNA in rats with diabetic retinopathy. *Chin Med J (Engl), 116,* 478-480.

[82] Dal Monte, M.; Cammalleri, M.; Martini, D.; Casini, G. & Bagnoli, P. (2007). Antiangiogenic role of somatostatin receptor 2 in a model of hypoxia-induced neovascularization in the retina: results from transgenic mice. *Invest Ophthalmol Vis Sci, 48,* 3480-3489.

[83] Leske, D. A.; Wu, J.; Fautsch, M. P.; Karger, R. A.; Berdahl, J. P.; Lanier, W. L. & Holmes, J. M. (2004). The role of VEGF and IGF-1 in a hypercarbic oxygen-induced retinopathy rat model of ROP. *Mol Vis, 10,* 43-50.

[84] Leske, D. A.; Wu, J.; Mookadam, M.; Chen, Y.; Fautsch, M. P.; Holmes, J. M. & Lanier, W. L. (2006). The relationship of retinal VEGF and

retinal IGF-1 mRNA with neovascularization in an acidosis-induced model of retinopathy of prematurity. *Curr Eye Res, 31,* 163-169.

[85] Averbukh, E.; Weiss, O.; Halpert, M.; Yanko, R.; Moshe, R.; Nephesh, I.; Flyvbjerg, A.; Yanko, L. & Raz, I. (1998). Gene expression of insulin-like growth factor-I, its receptor and binding proteins in retina under hypoxic conditions. *Metabolism, 47,* 1331-1336.

[86] Werdich, X. Q.; McCollum, G. W.; Rajaratnam, V. S. & Penn, J. S. (2004). Variable oxygen and retinal VEGF levels: correlation with incidence and severity of pathology in a rat model of oxygen-induced retinopathy. *Exp Eye Res, 79,* 623-630.

[87] Witmer, A. N.; Blaauwgeers, H. G.; Weich, H. A.; Alitalo, K.; Vrensen, G. F. & Schlingemann, R. O. (2002). Altered expression patterns of VEGF receptors in human diabetic retina and in experimental VEGF-induced retinopathy in monkey. *Invest Ophthalmol Vis Sci, 43,* 849-857.

[88] Witmer, A. N.; Vrensen, G. F.; Van Noorden, C. J. & Schlingemann, R. O. (2003). Vascular endothelial growth factors and angiogenesis in eye disease. *Prog Retin Eye Res, 22,* 1-29.

[89] McLeod, D. S.; Taomoto, M.; Cao, J.; Zhu, Z.; Witte, L. & Lutty, G. A. (2002). Localization of VEGF receptor-2 (KDR/Flk-1) and effects of blocking it in oxygen-induced retinopathy. *Invest Ophthalmol Vis Sci, 43,* 474-482.

[90] Ellis, E. A.; Guberski, D. L.; Somogyi-Mann, M. & Grant, M. B. (2000). Increased H2O2, vascular endothelial growth factor and receptors in the retina of the BBZ/Wor diabetic rat. *Free Radic Biol Med, 28,* 91-101.

[91] Gilbert, R. E.; Vranes, D.; Berka, J. L.; Kelly, D. J.; Cox, A.; Wu, L. L.; Stacker, S. A. & Cooper, M. E. (1998). Vascular endothelial growth factor and its receptors in control and diabetic rat eyes. *Lab Invest, 78,* 1017-1027.

[92] Prokosch, V.; Fink, J.; Heiduschka, P.; Melkonyan, H. & Thanos, S. (2011). VEGF, Ang-2 and SRIF associated abnormal postnatal development of the retinal capillary network in the Royal College of Surgeons rat. *Exp Eye Res, 92,* 128-137.

[93] Dal Monte, M.; Ristori, C.; Cammalleri, M. & Bagnoli, P. (2009). Effects of somatostatin analogues on retinal angiogenesis in a mouse model of oxygen-induced retinopathy: involvement of the somatostatin receptor subtype 2. *Invest Ophthalmol Vis Sci, 50,* 3596-3606.

[94] Bezerra, Y.; Fuselier, J. A.; Peyman, G. A.; Oner, H.; Drouant, G. & Coy, D. H. (2005). Study of inhibitory effects of an antiangiogenic

somatostatin-camptothecin conjugate on laser-induced choroidal neovascularization in rats. *Retina, 25,* 345-354.

[95] Palii, S. S.; Afzal, A.; Shaw, L. C.; Pan, H.; Caballero, S.; Miller, R. C.; Jurczyk, S.; Reubi, J. C.; Tan, Y.; Hochhaus, G.; Edelhauser, H.; Geroski, D.; Shapiro, G. & Grant, M. B. (2008). Nonpeptide somatostatin receptor agonists specifically target ocular neovascularization via the somatostatin type 2 receptor. *Invest Ophthalmol Vis Sci, 49,* 5094-5102.

[96] Wolkenberg, S. E.; Zhao, Z.; Thut, C.; Maxwell, J. W.; McDonald, T. P.; Kinose, F.; Reilly, M.; Lindsley, C. W. & Hartman, G. D. (2011). Design, synthesis, and evaluation of novel 3,6-diaryl-4-aminoalkoxyquinolines as selective agonists of somatostatin receptor subtype 2. *J Med Chem, 54,* 2351-2358.

[97] Ljubimov, A. V.; Caballero, S.; Aoki, A. M.; Pinna, L. A.; Grant, M. B. & Castellon, R. (2004). Involvement of protein kinase CK2 in angiogenesis and retinal neovascularization. *Invest Ophthalmol Vis Sci, 45,* 4583-4591.

[98] Kramerov, A. A.; Saghizadeh, M.; Caballero, S.; Shaw, L. C.; Li Calzi, S.; Bretner, M.; Montenarh, M.; Pinna, L. A.; Grant, M. B. & Ljubimov, A. V. (2008). Inhibition of protein kinase CK2 suppresses angiogenesis and hematopoietic stem cell recruitment to retinal neovascularization sites. *Mol Cell Biochem, 316,* 177-186.

[99] Kramerov, A. A.; Saghizadeh, M.; Pan, H.; Kabosova, A.; Montenarh, M.; Ahmed, K.; Penn, J. S.; Chan, C. K.; Hinton, D. R.; Grant, M. B. & Ljubimov, A. V. (2006). Expression of protein kinase CK2 in astroglial cells of normal and neovascularized retina. *Am J Pathol, 168,* 1722-1736.

[100] Dal Monte, M.; Ristori, C.; Videau, C.; Loudes, C.; Martini, D.; Casini, G.; Epelbaum, J. & Bagnoli, P. (2010). Expression, localization, and functional coupling of the somatostatin receptor subtype 2 in a mouse model of oxygen-induced retinopathy. *Invest Ophthalmol Vis Sci, 51,* 1848-1856.

[101] Mei, S.; Cammalleri, M.; Azara, D.; Casini, G.; Bagnoli, P. & Dal Monte, M. (2012). Mechanisms underlying somatostatin receptor 2 down-regulation of vascular endothelial growth factor expression in response to hypoxia in mouse retinal explants. *J Pathol, 226,* 519-533.

[102] Adams, R. L.; Adams, I. P.; Lindow, S. W.; Zhong, W. & Atkin, S. L. (2005). Somatostatin receptors 2 and 5 are preferentially expressed in proliferating endothelium. *Br J Cancer, 92,* 1493-1498.

[103] Watson, J. C.; Balster, D. A.; Gebhardt, B. M.; O'Dorisio, T. M.; O'Dorisio, M. S.; Espenan, G. D.; Drouant, G. J. & Woltering, E. A. (2001). Growing vascular endothelial cells express somatostatin subtype 2 receptors. *Br J Cancer, 85,* 266-272.

[104] Lambooij, A. C.; Kuijpers, R. W.; van Lichtenauer-Kaligis, E. G.; Kliffen, M.; Baarsma, G. S.; van Hagen, P. M. & Mooy, C. M. (2000). Somatostatin receptor 2A expression in choroidal neovascularization secondary to age-related macular degeneration. *Invest Ophthalmol Vis Sci, 41,* 2329-2335.

[105] Grant, M. B.; Caballero, S. & Millard, W. J. (1993). Inhibition of IGF-I and b-FGF stimulated growth of human retinal endothelial cells by the somatostatin analogue, octreotide: a potential treatment for ocular neovascularization. *Regul Pept, 48,* 267-278.

[106] Bocci, G.; Culler, M. D.; Fioravanti, A.; Orlandi, P.; Fasciani, A.; Colucci, R.; Taylor, J. E.; Sadat, D.; Danesi, R. & Del Tacca, M. (2007). *In vitro* antiangiogenic activity of selective somatostatin subtype-1 receptor agonists. *Eur J Clin Invest, 37,* 700-708.

[107] Wilson, S. H.; Davis, M. I.; Caballero, S. & Grant, M. B. (2001). Modulation of retinal endothelial cell behaviour by insulin-like growth factor I and somatostatin analogues: implications for diabetic retinopathy. *Growth Horm IGF Res, 11 Suppl A,* S53-59.

[108] Florio, T.; Morini, M.; Villa, V.; Arena, S.; Corsaro, A.; Thellung, S.; Culler, M. D.; Pfeffer, U.; Noonan, D. M.; Schettini, G. & Albini, A. (2003). Somatostatin inhibits tumor angiogenesis and growth via somatostatin receptor-3-mediated regulation of endothelial nitric oxide synthase and mitogen-activated protein kinase activities. *Endocrinology, 144,* 1574-1584.

[109] Ristori, C.; Ferretti, M. E.; Pavan, B.; Cervellati, F.; Casini, G.; Catalani, E.; Dal Monte, M. & Biondi, C. (2008). Adenylyl cyclase/cAMP system involvement in the antiangiogenic effect of somatostatin in the retina. Results from transgenic mice. *Neurochem Res, 33,* 1247-1255.

[110] Arjamaa, O. & Nikinmaa, M. (2006). Oxygen-dependent diseases in the retina: role of hypoxia-inducible factors. *Exp Eye Res, 83,* 473-483.

[111] Bartoli, M.; Al-Shabrawey, M.; Labazi, M.; Behzadian, M. A.; Istanboli, M.; El-Remessy, A. B.; Caldwell, R. W.; Marcus, D. M. & Caldwell, R. B. (2009). HMG-CoA reductase inhibitors (statin) prevents retinal neovascularization in a model of oxygen-induced retinopathy. *Invest Ophthalmol Vis Sci, 50,* 4934-4940.

[112] Gariboldi, M. B.; Ravizza, R. & Monti, E. (2010). The IGFR1 inhibitor NVP-AEW541 disrupts a pro-survival and pro-angiogenic IGF-STAT3-HIF1 pathway in human glioblastoma cells. *Biochem Pharmacol, 80,* 455-462.

[113] Jung, J. E.; Kim, H. S.; Lee, C. S.; Park, D. H.; Kim, Y. N.; Lee, M. J.; Lee, J. W.; Park, J. W.; Kim, M. S.; Ye, S. K. & Chung, M. H. (2007). Caffeic acid and its synthetic derivative CADPE suppress tumor angiogenesis by blocking STAT3-mediated VEGF expression in human renal carcinoma cells. *Carcinogenesis, 28,* 1780-1787.

[114] Xu, Q.; Briggs, J.; Park, S.; Niu, G.; Kortylewski, M.; Zhang, S.; Gritsko, T.; Turkson, J.; Kay, H.; Semenza, G. L.; Cheng, J. Q.; Jove, R. & Yu, H. (2005). Targeting Stat3 blocks both HIF-1 and VEGF expression induced by multiple oncogenic growth signaling pathways. *Oncogene, 24,* 5552-5560.

[115] Villaume, K.; Blanc, M.; Gouysse, G.; Walter, T.; Couderc, C.; Nejjari, M.; Vercherat, C.; Cordier-Bussat, M.; Roche, C. & Scoazec, J. Y. (2010). VEGF secretion by neuroendocrine tumor cells is inhibited by octreotide and by inhibitors of the PI3K/AKT/mTOR pathway. *Neuroendocrinology, 91,* 268-278.

[116] Florio, T. (2008). Molecular mechanisms of the antiproliferative activity of somatostatin receptors (SSTRs) in neuroendocrine tumors. *Front Biosci, 13,* 822-840.

[117] Bhattacharya, R.; Kwon, J.; Wang, E.; Mukherjee, P. & Mukhopadhyay, D. (2008). Src homology 2 (SH2) domain containing protein tyrosine phosphatase-1 (SHP-1) dephosphorylates VEGF Receptor-2 and attenuates endothelial DNA synthesis, but not migration*. *J Mol Signal, 3,* 8.

[118] Cezar-de-Mello, P. F.; Vieira, A. M.; Nascimento-Silva, V.; Villela, C. G.; Barja-Fidalgo, C. & Fierro, I. M. (2008). ATL-1, an analogue of aspirin-triggered lipoxin A4, is a potent inhibitor of several steps in angiogenesis induced by vascular endothelial growth factor. *Br J Pharmacol, 153,* 956-965.

[119] Sugano, M.; Tsuchida, K.; Maeda, T. & Makino, N. (2007). SiRNA targeting SHP-1 accelerates angiogenesis in a rat model of hindlimb ischemia. *Atherosclerosis, 191,* 33-39.

[120] Shumak, S. L.; Grossman, L. D.; Chew, E.; Kozousek, V.; George, S. R.; Singer, W.; Harris, A. G. & Zinman, B. (1990). Growth hormone suppression and nonproliferative diabetic retinopathy: a preliminary feasibility study. *Clin Invest Med, 13,* 287-292.

[121] Kirkegaard, C.; Norgaard, K.; Snorgaard, O.; Bek, T.; Larsen, M. & Lund-Andersen, H. (1990). Effect of one year continuous subcutaneous infusion of a somatostatin analogue, octreotide, on early retinopathy, metabolic control and thyroid function in Type I (insulin-dependent) diabetes mellitus. *Acta Endocrinol (Copenh), 122,* 766-772.

[122] Clemens, A.; Klevesath, M. S.; Hofmann, M.; Raulf, F.; Henkels, M.; Amiral, J.; Seibel, M. J.; Zimmermann, J.; Ziegler, R.; Wahl, P. & Nawroth, P. P. (1999). Octreotide (somatostatin analog) treatment reduces endothelial cell dysfunction in patients with diabetes mellitus. *Metabolism, 48,* 1236-1240.

[123] McCombe, M.; Lightman, S.; Eckland, D. J.; Hamilton, A. M. & Lightman, S. L. (1991). Effect of a long-acting somatostatin analogue (BIM23014) on proliferative diabetic retinopathy: a pilot study. *Eye (Lond), 5 (Pt 5),* 569-575.

[124] Mallet, B.; Vialettes, B.; Haroche, S.; Escoffier, P.; Gastaut, P.; Taubert, J. P. & Vague, P. (1992). Stabilization of severe proliferative diabetic retinopathy by long-term treatment with SMS 201-995. *Diabete Metab, 18,* 438-444.

[125] Grant, M. B.; Mames, R. N.; Fitzgerald, C.; Hazariwala, K. M.; Cooper-DeHoff, R.; Caballero, S. & Estes, K. S. (2000). The efficacy of octreotide in the therapy of severe nonproliferative and early proliferative diabetic retinopathy: a randomized controlled study. *Diabetes Care, 23,* 504-509.

[126] Boehm, B. O.; Lang, G. K.; Jehle, P. M.; Feldman, B. & Lang, G. E. (2001). Octreotide reduces vitreous hemorrhage and loss of visual acuity risk in patients with high-risk proliferative diabetic retinopathy. *Horm Metab Res, 33,* 300-306.

[127] Hernaez-Ortega, M. C.; Soto-Pedre, E. & Pinies, J. A. (2008). Lanreotide Autogel for persistent diabetic macular edema. *Diabetes Res Clin Pract, 80,* e8-10.

[128] Hernaez-Ortega, M. C.; Soto-Pedre, E. & Martin, J. J. (2004). Sandostatin LAR for cystoid diabetic macular edema: a 1-year experience. *Diabetes Res Clin Pract, 64,* 71-72.

[129] Shah, S. M.; Nguyen, Q. D.; Mir, H. S.; Polito, A.; Hafiz, G.; Tatlipinar, S.; Do, D. V.; Vitale, S. & Haller, J. A. (2010). A randomized, double-masked controlled clinical trial of Sandostatin long-acting release depot in patients with postsurgical cystoid macular edema. *Retina, 30,* 160-166.

[130] Hogewind, B. F.; Pieters, G. & Hoyng, C. B. (2008). Octreotide acetate in dominant cystoid macular dystrophy. *Eur J Ophthalmol, 18,* 99-103.

[131] Barber, A. J. (2003). A new view of diabetic retinopathy: a neurodegenerative disease of the eye. *Prog Neuropsychopharmacol Biol Psychiatry, 27,* 283-290.

[132] Villarroel, M.; Ciudin, A.; Hernandez, C. & Simo, R. (2010). Neurodegeneration: An early event of diabetic retinopathy. *World J Diabetes, 1,* 57-64.

[133] Hernandez, C. & Simo, R. (2012). Neuroprotection in diabetic retinopathy. *Curr Diab Rep, 12,* 329-337.

[134] Lorenzi, M. & Gerhardinger, C. (2001). Early cellular and molecular changes induced by diabetes in the retina. *Diabetologia, 44,* 791-804.

[135] Asnaghi, V.; Gerhardinger, C.; Hoehn, T.; Adeboje, A. & Lorenzi, M. (2003). A role for the polyol pathway in the early neuroretinal apoptosis and glial changes induced by diabetes in the rat. *Diabetes, 52,* 506-511.

[136] Carrasco, E.; Hernandez, C.; Miralles, A.; Huguet, P.; Farres, J. & Simo, R. (2007). Lower somatostatin expression is an early event in diabetic retinopathy and is associated with retinal neurodegeneration. *Diabetes Care, 30,* 2902-2908.

[137] Carrasco, E.; Hernandez, C.; de Torres, I.; Farres, J. & Simo, R. (2008). Lowered cortistatin expression is an early event in the human diabetic retina and is associated with apoptosis and glial activation. *Mol Vis, 14,* 1496-1502.

[138] Simo, R.; Carrasco, E.; Fonollosa, A.; Garcia-Arumi, J.; Casamitjana, R. & Hernandez, C. (2007). Deficit of somatostatin in the vitreous fluid of patients with diabetic macular edema. *Diabetes Care, 30,* 725-727.

[139] Dal Monte, M.; Latina, V.; Cupisti, E. & Bagnoli, P. (2012). Protective role of somatostatin receptor 2 against retinal degeneration in response to hypoxia. *Naunyn Schmiedebergs Arch Pharmacol, 385,* 481-494.

[140] Osborne, N. N.; Casson, R. J.; Wood, J. P.; Chidlow, G.; Graham, M. & Melena, J. (2004). Retinal ischemia: mechanisms of damage and potential therapeutic strategies. *Prog Retin Eye Res, 23,* 91-147.

[141] Antonetti, D. A.; Barber, A. J.; Bronson, S. K.; Freeman, W. M.; Gardner, T. W.; Jefferson, L. S.; Kester, M.; Kimball, S. R.; Krady, J. K.; LaNoue, K. F.; Norbury, C. C.; Quinn, P. G.; Sandirasegarane, L. & Simpson, I. A. (2006). Diabetic retinopathy: seeing beyond glucose-induced microvascular disease. *Diabetes, 55,* 2401-2411.

[142] Antonetti, D. A.; Klein, R. & Gardner, T. W. (2012). Diabetic retinopathy. *N Engl J Med, 366,* 1227-1239.

[143] Dal Monte, M.; Petrucci, C.; Cozzi, A.; Allen, J. P. & Bagnoli, P. (2003). Somatostatin inhibits potassium-evoked glutamate release by activation of the sst(2) somatostatin receptor in the mouse retina. *Naunyn Schmiedebergs Arch Pharmacol, 367,* 188-192.

[144] Kiagiadaki, F. & Thermos, K. (2008). Effect of intravitreal administration of somatostatin and sst2 analogs on AMPA-induced neurotoxicity in rat retina. *Invest Ophthalmol Vis Sci, 49,* 3080-3089.

[145] Kiagiadaki, F.; Savvaki, M. & Thermos, K. (2010). Activation of somatostatin receptor (sst 5) protects the rat retina from AMPA-induced neurotoxicity. *Neuropharmacology, 58,* 297-303.

[146] Stitt, A. W.; O'Neill, C. L.; O'Doherty, M. T.; Archer, D. B.; Gardiner, T. A. & Medina, R. J. (2011). Vascular stem cells and ischaemic retinopathies. *Prog Retin Eye Res, 30,* 149-166.

[147] Minhas, G.; Morishita, R. & Anand, A. (2012). Preclinical models to investigate retinal ischemia: advances and drawbacks. *Front Neurol, 3,* 75.

[148] Bek, T. (2009). Inner retinal ischaemia: current understanding and needs for further investigations. *Acta Ophthalmol, 87,* 362-367.

[149] Fulton, A. B.; Akula, J. D.; Mocko, J. A.; Hansen, R. M.; Benador, I. Y.; Beck, S. C.; Fahl, E.; Seeliger, M. W.; Moskowitz, A. & Harris, M. E. (2009). Retinal degenerative and hypoxic ischemic disease. *Doc Ophthalmol, 118,* 55-61.

[150] Sapieha, P.; Hamel, D.; Shao, Z.; Rivera, J. C.; Zaniolo, K.; Joyal, J. S. & Chemtob, S. (2010). Proliferative retinopathies: angiogenesis that blinds. *Int J Biochem Cell Biol, 42,* 5-12.

[151] Celiker, U.; Ilhan, N.; Ozercan, I.; Demir, T. & Celiker, H. (2002). Octreotide reduces ischaemia-reperfusion injury in the retina. *Acta Ophthalmol Scand, 80,* 395-400.

[152] Mastrodimou, N.; Lambrou, G. N. & Thermos, K. (2005). Effect of somatostatin analogues on chemically induced ischaemia in the rat retina. *Naunyn Schmiedebergs Arch Pharmacol, 371,* 44-53.

[153] Catalani, E.; Cervia, D.; Martini, D.; Bagnoli, P.; Simonetti, E.; Timperio, A. M. & Casini, G. (2007). Changes in neuronal response to ischemia in retinas with genetic alterations of somatostatin receptor expression. *Eur J Neurosci, 25,* 1447-1459.

[154] Cervia, D.; Martini, D.; Ristori, C.; Catalani, E.; Timperio, A. M.; Bagnoli, P. & Casini, G. (2008). Modulation of the neuronal response to ischaemia by somatostatin analogues in wild-type and knock-out mouse retinas. *J Neurochem, 106,* 2224-2235.

[155] Vasilaki, A.; Sourlas, V.; Athanasiou, V.; Kouvaras, E. & Asprodini, E. K. (2008). Octreotide influences ischemia-induced [3H]D-aspartate release and GABA immunoreactivity changes in rat retinal and hippocampal preparations. *FENS Abstr, 4,* 051.039.

[156] Meriney, S. D.; Gray, D. B. & Pilar, G. R. (1994). Somatostatin-induced inhibition of neuronal Ca2+ current modulated by cGMP-dependent protein kinase. *Nature, 369,* 336-339.

[157] Koch, K. W.; Lambrecht, H. G.; Haberecht, M.; Redburn, D. & Schmidt, H. H. (1994). Functional coupling of a Ca2+/calmodulin-dependent nitric oxide synthase and a soluble guanylyl cyclase in vertebrate photoreceptor cells. *Embo J, 13,* 3312-3320.

[158] Ding, J. D. & Weinberg, R. J. (2007). Distribution of soluble guanylyl cyclase in rat retina. *J Comp Neurol, 500,* 734-745.

[159] Mastrodimou, N.; Kiagiadaki, F.; Hodjarova, M.; Karagianni, E. & Thermos, K. (2006). Somatostatin receptors (sst2) regulate cGMP production in rat retina. *Regul Pept, 133,* 41-46.

[160] Cervia, D.; Catalani, E.; Dal Monte, M. & Casini, G. (2012). Vascular endothelial growth factor in the ischemic retina and its regulation by somatostatin. *J Neurochem, 120,* 818-829.

[161] Trovati, M.; Massara, F.; Camanni, F.; Molinatti, G. M.; Lorenzati, R. & Pagano, G. F. (1980). Effect of the somatostatin analog D-Trp8,D-Cys14 on glucose insulin, pancreatic glucagon and growth hormone plasma levels in acromegalics and mild diabetics. *J Endocrinol Invest, 3,* 189-192.

[162] Gerich, J. E. (1986). Rationale for inhibition of growth hormone secretion in the management of the diabetic patient. *Scand J Gastroenterol Suppl, 119,* 154-157.

[163] Nakano, T.; Harano, Y.; Emura, J.; Kimura, T.; Sakakibara, S. & Shigeta, Y. (1986). Development of specific and non-specific somatostatin analogs. *Horm Metab Res, 18,* 98-102.

In: Somatostatin   ISBN: 978-1-62417-419-3
Editors: A. Anderson and T. McAnulty © 2013 Nova Science Publishers, Inc.

Chapter 2

RADIOLABELLED SOMATOSTATIN ANALOGUES FOR USE IN MOLECULAR IMAGING

Elisabeth Blom and Jacek Koziorowski*

Dept. Clinical Physiology, Herlev University Hospital,
Herlev Ringvej, Herlev, Denmark

ABSTRACT

Being able to monitor tumours and their response to treatment is essential in therapy planning. Somatostatin receptor (SSTR) positive tumours, there among neuroendocrine tumours, can be imaged by using radiolabelled somatostatin analogues. In the late 1980's the first radiolabelled somatostatin analogue was reported. A few years later the gamma emitting tracer which still is considered the golden standard, $[^{111}In\text{-}DTPA^0]$octreotide (OctreoScan), was introduced. From that point a number of analogues labelled with various nuclides for imaging techniques like scintigraphy, single photon emission computed tomography (SPECT) and positron emission tomography (PET) have been developed to obtain improved imaging properties. The five subtypes of SSTR (sst_{1-5}) are unequally distributed in SSTR-positive malignancies, and the structures of the somatostatin analogues are therefore varied to obtain high binding affinity for each. Development of PET octreotide

* E-mail: elisabeth.blom@heh.regionh.dk.

tracers has made high resolution imaging possible. The positron emitting nuclide ^{68}Ga is conveniently obtained from an easy to handle ^{68}Ge/^{68}Ga generator. Several of the ^{68}Ga-labelled octreotide derivatives, like DOTA-TOC (DOTA-D-Phe^1-Tyr^3-octreotide), DOTA-TATE (DOTA-Tyr^3-octreotate) and DOTA-NOC (DOTA-1-Nal^3-octreotide), have superior pharmacological properties compared to OctreoScan. These derivatives can also be labelled with therapeutic nuclides like ^{90}Y and ^{177}Lu and consequently used as theranostic pairs.

The intention of this chapter is to give an overview of available somatostatin analogues labelled with radioactive isotopes and their use in molecular imaging. Focus will be made on analogues labelled with PET nuclides, ^{68}Ga in particular.

INTRODUCTION

Neuroendocrine tumours (NETs) are a heterogenous group of malignancies, where the gastroenteropancreatic NETs (GEP-NETs) are the largest group. GEP-NETs originate from either pancreas or gastrointestinal tract. Of all malignant gastrointestinal tumours 2% consist of GEP-NETs [1]. The incidence of NETs has increased considerably over the last 30 years [2, 3]. The delay for diagnosis is usually 5-7 years, due to the lack of specifically connected symptoms and methods for early screening [4]. Therefore the patients are not diagnosed until they have reached an advanced state of the disease. The diagnosis can be difficult due to the fact that the NET tumours and metastases can occur in small lesions and in many different parts of the body. The metabolic rate in lesions is also usually slow. Methods for early diagnosis and treatment not only for tumour, but also for metastases are highly desirable. The primary treatment of GEP-NETs today is surgical resection, also in patients which have developed metastases. Cytoreduction surgery can help the patients with metastases by prolonging their life-time and also improving their quality of life and working ability [5]. An important role is already played by molecular imaging in staging and follow-up on treatment. Increased surgical precision is achieved after more precise imaging, reducing the distress for the patient with less risk of leaving undetected metastases behind. Previously diagnostics of NETs have been performed using morphological imaging techniques like magnetic resonance imaging (MRI), computed tomography (CT) and ultrasonography (US) in combination with whole-body somatostatin receptor scintigraphy (SRS) [6, 7].

Somatostatin (SST) is a small, cyclic 14-amino-acid peptide hormone [8] produced by the hypothalamus inhibiting release of secretory proteins like growth hormone (somatotropin), glucagon, insulin and gastrin [9, 10]. Somatostatin is expressed in other parts body as well, including different endocrine organs, pancreas (by β-cells), gastrointestinal tract and the immune system [11].

Somatostatin receptors are G-protein coupled membrane glycoproteins which are internalized after the specific ligand has bound [12]. All of the five somatostatin receptors (sst$_{1-5}$) are expressed in many NETs, and in most GEP-NETs [13]. The SST receptors are also expressed in peritumoral vessels and in inflammatory and immune cells [14]. The receptor sst$_2$ is commonly overexpressed in GEP-NETs [15], making it useful as a target for imaging and therapy.

Using radiolabelled somatostatin analogues is the preferred strategy for therapy for functional NETs as they have antitumour effects as well as making reduction of hormone-related symptoms possible [15]. The interaction between the receptor and the somatostatin analogues is mediated by interaction with specific cell membrane receptors on target cells [14]. Also the radiolabelled peptide is retained by means of internalization of the complex between the peptide and the receptor [14]. Somatostatin has been modified into different analogues to extend its half-life in blood, being only 2-4 min. The use of analogues of somatostatin labelled with nuclides for therapy and imaging in theranostic pairs, has led to improvements in the management of GEP-NETs [16]. The golden standard since over 20 years, [^{111}In-DTPA^0]octreotide (OctreoScan) will most probably in the future be replaced by ^{68}Ga-labelled octreotide tracers due to their higher sensitivity and specificity, fast scanning protocol, and simple mode of preparation [17].

This chapter gives an overview of molecular imaging using radiolabelled somatostatin analogues with focus of imaging using positron emission tomography (PET) and ^{68}Ga-labelled octreotides in particular.

RADIOLABELLED SOMATOSTATIN ANALOGUES

Somatostatin analogues have been labelled with a large variety of radioactive nuclides, like diagnostic γ emitters; ^{123}I [9, 18], ^{99m}Tc [19, 20], ^{111}In [9], and ^{67}Ga [21], positron emitters; ^{11}C [22], ^{18}F [23-26], ^{76}Br [27], ^{66}Ga [28], ^{110m}In [29], ^{86}Y [30, 31], ^{44}Sc [32], and ^{64}Cu [33-39] and also with particle emitters like ^{90}Y [16, 40, 41], ^{177}Lu [42] and ^{213}Bi [43]. Currently a lot of attention is paid to ^{68}Ga-labelled octreotides.

Somatostatin Receptor Scintigraphy (SRS) with [^{111}In-DTPA^0]Octreotide (Octreoscan)

The first developed somatostatin analogue for somatostatin receptor scintigraphy (SRS) was labelled with ^{123}I [44, 45], but this tracer had many drawbacks, like gastrointestinal excretion interfering with tumour uptake in the abdominal region [46]. Thereafter followed analogues labelled with ^{111}In [47, 48], ^{99m}Tc [49] and ^{68}Ga [49]. [^{111}In-DTPA^0]octreotide (OctreoScan, Mallinckrodt, St. Louis, MO, DTPA= 2-[bis[2-[bis(carboxymethyl) amino]ethyl]amino]acetic acid, Figure 1) [47] was the first registered radiopeptide and was in 1994 approved by the Food and Drug Administration (FDA). Still today OctreoScan is considered the golden standard in NET imaging [50] in combination with SRS [51, 52] or single photon emission computed tomography (SPECT) [53]. SPECT imaging is nowadays usually combined with computed tomography (CT) for improved functional information in combination with anatomical localisation [54, 55].

Indium-111 has a half-life of 67.4 h, γ photon energies of 171 and 245 keV, and decays to ^{111}Cd by electron capture (EC). The production requires a cyclotron and the ^{111}In is produced by the nuclear reaction ^{112}Cd(p, 2n)^{111}In. The long half-life renders distribution of ^{111}In over a large area from the cyclotron location. Indium also emits Auger electrons with short penetration range (0.02-10 μm) in tissue which also makes this nuclide applicable for therapy. In aqueous solution indium is most stable in its 3+ form [56], and it can form complexes with chelators like DTPA and DOTA.

OctreoScan has affinity for sst_2 and its sensitivity for the detection of NETs is usually 67-100% [57, 58]. The limitations of SRS occur in organs like the liver [59], where the physiological uptake is high. Low spatial resolution and high limit of detection make identification of small lesions difficult, even when using SPECT [60]. Whole-body SPECT is not routinely used, but the generally performed SRS gives lower sensitivity than SPECT.

OctreoScan imaging is usually performed 24 and 48 h post injection to await the renal excretion to obtain images with higher contrast [14]. In patients treated with non-radioactive somatostatin compounds it might be necessary to stop the treatment before imaging, depending on the properties of the treating substance [61].

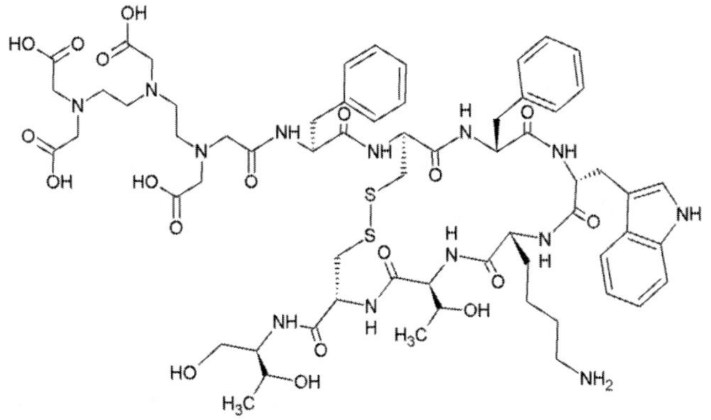

Figure 1. DTPA-octreotide (precursor of OctreoScan).

OctreoScan is highly stable *in vivo*. After 4 h ^{111}In is still bound to the intact peptide. Renal excretion is the main excretion route, with 25% of the radioactivity in the urine after 3 h and 90% after 48h [62].

OctreoScan is widely used for imaging of neuroendocrine tumours like carcinoids, gastrinomas, paragangliomas, pheochromocytomas, medullary thyroid cancers (MTC), meningioma and anterior pituitary adenomas [9, 63-66], also for monitoring treatment response [65, 67, 68]. Recently the use of OctreoScan and fused SPECT/MRI in pancreatic insulinoma allowing precise localisation of tumour was reported [69].

Positron Emission Tomography

Positron emission tomography (PET) is a non-invasive *in vivo* imaging technique that allows the localization of a molecule labelled with positron-emitting nuclides [70].

PET is increasingly used as a diagnostic tool in major medical fields such as oncology, neurology and cardiology [71].

Positron-emitting radionuclides are neutron-deficient and decay by emitting positrons (β^+). After travelling a few millimetres the positron stops and is annihilated when it encounters its antiparticle, an electron. The annihilation generates two high-energy photons (511 keV) travelling along trajectories $180 \pm 0.25°$ apart.

Photons are registered as originating from the same decay event if they arrive simultaneously at two antipodal detectors in the circular PET scanner; this is called coincidence detection (Figure 2). The distribution of the radioactivity is then visualized and quantified using a computerized image-reconstructing algorithm.

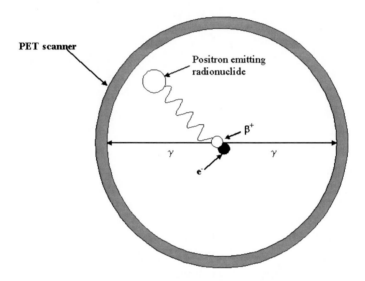

Figure 2. Schematic description of β^+ annihilation and coincidence detection in a PET scanner ($\gamma = 511$ keV).

In PET the strategy is, unlike in for example CT, to find abnormalities before the morphological changes occur and also to investigate the function of metabolic pathways in the tissue, using a specific radiolabelled tracer. Currently, over 90% of NETs can be imaged by existing PET tracers [14].

PET in combination with CT gives fused images making correlation of anatomical location and function possible [72]. A PET scan can be performed 1 h post injection of the ^{68}Ga containing compound whereas for the SRS the delay is 24-48 h. The spatial resolution is 2-6 mm for PET compared to scintigraphy where it is 10-15 mm, and also with regards to volume sensitivity PET is superior (8.3 times higher than for SPECT) [72, 73]. High spatial resolution is very important in the case of small lesions (<10 mm) which often occur in NETs. Furthermore, the PET technique makes the uptake of the tracer quantifiable.

The exposure to radiation for the patient is reduced when using ^{68}Ga-labelled tracer [74] since the whole investigation can be completed within 2 h and the half-life of the nuclide is short (68 min).

PET in SST Imaging

In imaging of NETs the widely used PET tracer 2-[^{18}F]fluoro-2-deoxy-D-glucose ([^{18}F]FDG) is not useful due to its low sensitivity for detection of tumours which are growing slowly and having low metabolism [75]. [^{18}F]FDG can however be useful in some cases where the NETs are showing an aggressive behaviour [76], or having low expression of SST, i.e. low differentiated or e.g. MTC [77-79]. [^{124}I]Iodide is also a useful tracer for MTC [80-82].

^{68}Ga-Labelled Somatostatin Analogues

The first prepared ^{68}Ga-labelled somatostatin analogue was [^{68}Ga]DFO-octreotide [21] (DFO = desferrioxamine B). This tracer was however not taken further to clinical use. Octreotide analogues labelled with ^{68}Ga have the potential to dominate the diagnostics of NETs in the future.

The sensitivity in detection of GEP-NET tumours is very high (80-100%) for the three ^{68}Ga-labelled octreotide analogues DOTA-TOC (DOTA-D-Phe^1-Tyr^3-octreotide) [60, 79, 83-85], DOTA-TATE (DOTA-Tyr^3-octreotate) [78, 86, 87] and DOTA-NOC (DOTA-1-Nal^3-octreotide) [88, 89] (Figure 3). They are all usually more sensitive and specific compared to [^{18}F]FDG [60, 78, 79] or [^{18}F]FDOPA [86, 88].

All three ^{68}Ga-labelled octreotides can bind to sst$_2$ [90]. DOTA-TOC also has affinity for sst$_5$. DOTA-TATE is known to have excellent affinity for sst$_2$, but low or nonexistent affinity for other SSTR [91]. DOTA-NOC was reported in 2003 to have high affinity also for the sst$_3$ and sst$_5$ [92]. The affinities of [^{68}Ga]DOTA-TOC, and OctreoScan in binding to sst$_2$ have been reported to be 2.5 ± 0.5 nM and 22 ± 3.6 nM respectively [91]. At this point there is no clear evidence of differences in imaging arising from the variations in affinity the SSTR for the three ^{68}Ga tracers, and consequently none of them is preferred over the other.

The sensitivity in the PET/CT image will depend on the density of SSTR in the specific tumour. Ending SST treatment before imaging usually needs to be considered, but the authors of one report claims that the treatment does not reduce tumour uptake of [^{68}Ga]DOTA-TATE. In 2011 Haug et al [93] reported a contradicting finding.

In spite of on-going treatment with a long-acting SST analogue no significant reduction of [^{68}Ga]DOTA-TATE binding in NETs but instead an improvement of the tumour to non-tumour ratio was observed.

Especially the combination PET/CT can give a high accuracy for e.g. liver metastases. CT provides additional information like individual anatomy, and PET can for example detect bone metastases often not recognised by CT. Fusion of the two images reveals an image closer to truth than using the two techniques individually.

In lung and bone the imaging results in NETs for [^{68}Ga]DOTA-TOC PET is superior to OctreoScan, and similar in brain and liver [94]. Especially bone and lungs are optimal targets for imaging using radiolabelled octreotide analogues. In the tumour lesions expressing SSTR the non-specific accumulation of DOTA-TOC is low and the tumour to non-tumour ratio is high [94]. SSTR is physiologically expressed in liver cells making hepatic somatostatin imaging more difficult. In some cases due to the high specificity of the ^{68}Ga-labelled octreotides the results can be over-interpreted.

The higher resolution in imaging is due to higher spatial resolution of the PET technique, advantageous pharmacokinetics of the ^{68}Ga peptides, and physical properties of ^{68}Ga [95]. The half-life of 68 min is a good match to the pharmacokinetics of many peptides reaching its target, diffusing and clearing from the blood quickly.

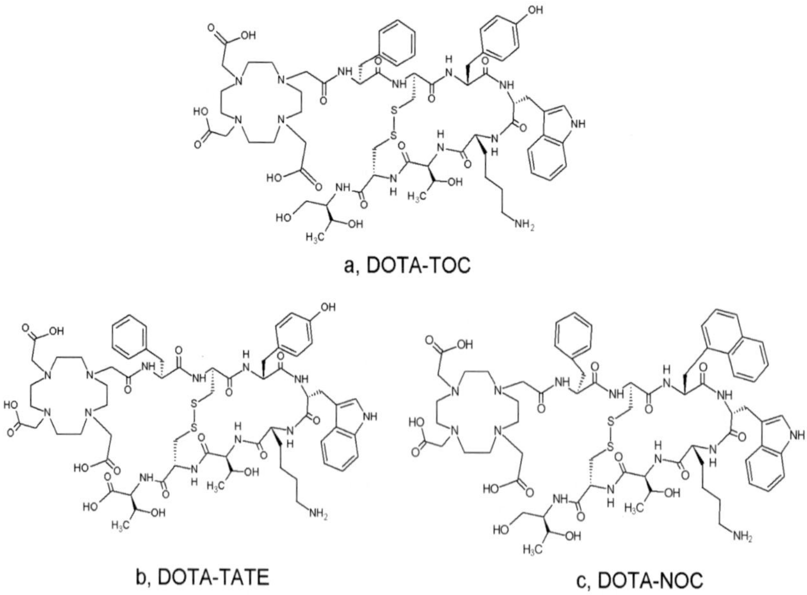

a, DOTA-TOC

b, DOTA-TATE

c, DOTA-NOC

Figure 3. Molecular structures of a, DOTA-TOC; b, DOTA-TATE and c, DOTA-NOC.

The functional information which can be obtained from SSTR imaging is an important complement to that obtained from morphological techniques like CT or MRI. Especially the fused scanners like SPECT/CT and PET/CT has greatly improved the possibilities to perform fast and highly resolved images. The recently introduced PET/MRI will bring new interesting imaging possibilities.

Peptide Receptor Radionuclide Therapy (PRRT)

Being able to accurately detect the somatostatin receptors in low amounts also makes specifically targeted radiotherapy possible. In peptide receptor radionuclide therapy (PRRT) the fact that NETs in many cases overexpress SSTR uniformly and also internalize the radiolabelled SST analogues thereby delivering cytotoxic doses of radiation specifically localized to the lesion, is used [96-99].

When using the same molecule labelled with a therapeutic radionuclide only the tumour or metastases are subjected to the radiation giving a more efficient treatment which is gentler for the rest of the body. Small tumours and metastases which could not be detected using methods like SRS or CT can be detected with the use of PET/CT in combination with ^{68}Ga-labelled octreotide analogues and the treatment and consequently the prognosis for survival is improved.

In a theranostic system molecular imaging is used for identifying a target for which the therapy is intended. Using molecular imaging makes a non-invasive mean of diagnosis and a personalized treatment possible. The great interest in theranostics is due to that it allows selection of therapy based on the molecular properties of the disease and also follow-up on the response of the therapy [100]. Reasonably a correlation is observed between positive SST expression in imaging and the response to treatment with therapeutic SST analogues [52, 101].

The first SST analogue used in PRRT was OctreoScan, where the Auger and internal conversion electrons from ^{111}In are employed for treatment of metastatic NETs. Improvement in symptoms was observed, but objective tumour responses were rare and short term. Using ^{111}In in peptides for radiotherapy is not favourable due to the small particle range, short tissue penetration (~10 μm) and its radiotoxicity (especially in bone marrow) [102]. Peptides labelled with β$^-$-emitters like ^{90}Y and ^{177}Lu are preferred because of the higher energy of the emitted particles which can damage the cell without penetrating too far into the surrounding tissue [102, 103].

DOTA-TOC labelled with ^{90}Y was the second applied SST compound for PRRT. Complete or partial remission was observed in 10-34% of investigated NET patients [16, 40, 104-106]. Thirdly [^{177}Lu]DOTA-TATE was introduced. Lutetium-177 does not only emit β$^-$ particles but also low energy γ rays and this makes direct dosimetry and post-therapy imaging possible [107]. Therapy using [^{177}Lu]DOTA-TATE was reported to give response in 30-38% of studied NET patients [103, 108-110]. Combination treatment including both [^{90}Y]DOTA-TOC and [^{177}Lu]DOTA-TATE has been shown to be the most promising approach. The high energy emitter ^{90}Y effects the larger tumours while the low energy emitter ^{177}Lu acts on the smaller lesions and metastases [102, 111].

A recent initial study by Ezziddin et al [112] showed that [^{68}Ga]DOTA-TOC imaging may predict absorbed [^{177}Lu]DOTA-octreotate doses in tumour. A low SUV indicating insufficient target irradiation could contribute in selection of appropriate patients for PRRT.

As an evidence of the usefulness of SST imaging in determining outcome after PRRT a study including patients having well differentiated NETs showed a correlation between decreased [^{68}Ga]DOTA-TATE uptake in tumours and an improvement in clinical symptoms [113].

PRRT is in general a safe method of treatment, especially when compared to chemotherapy, and severe side-effects are rare [114]. The importance of PRRT in treatment of patients with inoperable or metastatic GEP-NETs will increase [115, 116].

Synthesis of ^{68}Ga-Labelled Somatostatin Analogues

Gallium-68 is conveniently obtained from a commercially available ^{68}Ge/^{68}Ga generator, eliminating the need for a considerably more expensive cyclotron [117]. The half-life of ^{68}Ga (68 min) is an advantage with regards to radiation dose for the patient and compatibility with the pharmacokinetics of most peptides used for imaging [118].

Its mother nuclide ^{68}Ge has a half-life of 270.8 d making the shelf-life of the generator at least one year, depending on ^{68}Ge activity and ^{68}Ga activity requirements. Gallium-68 decays by β$^+$ (89%) and EC (11%) The energy of the γ photons arising from β$^+$ (positron) annihilation is 511 keV which is used for detection in the PET camera. These physical properties make ^{68}Ga more suitable for imaging than ^{111}In.

^{68}Ge/^{68}Ga generators can be based on titanium or tin dioxide, or an organic non-metallic resin as the stationary phase. The ^{68}Ga is eluted from the generator, typically in diluted hydrochloric acid, and can be either fractionated, or preconcentrated by cationic or anionic exchange [119]. These procedures are performed to obtain maximum amount of radioactivity in a minimal volume and remove possible metallic contaminants. The generator can be eluted several times per day. Gallium ions form gallium hydroxide at physiological pH and have highest stability as a 3+ ion in an aqueous solution [56]. Gallium forms complexes with coordination number 4 to 6 and not higher with compounds which contain nitrogen and oxygen atoms serving as electron donors [120].

The ^{68}Ge/^{68}Ga generator will probably in the future have a role like the ^{99}Mo/^{99m}Tc generator in clinical diagnostics, with the advantage of the considerably longer half-life of ^{68}Ge (270.8 days) compared to ^{99}Mo (66 h).

The ^{68}Ga(III) cation can be attached to the peptide using a chelator like the commonly used DOTA. A buffer is added to the reaction mixture to obtain the desired pH (4.6-5.0). Standard conditions for this labelling reaction are 90 °C for 10 min. Total synthesis can be performed in less than 30 min including quality control, usually consisting of either high performance liquid chromatography (HPLC) or instantaneous thin layer chromatography (ITLC). Both semi and fully automated systems are available for ^{68}Ga-labelling synthesis. A European Pharmacopoeia draft monograph proposal is available for the preparation of [^{68}Ga]DOTA-TOC [121].

A new strategy has been proposed for the ^{68}Ga-labelling of DOTA-TATE and DOTA-NOC. When using this method the labelling is performed at 121 °C for 15 min, which are the conditions for steam sterilization (autoclaving), thereby omitting the need for sterile filtration [122].

The macrocyclic chelator DOTA has the advantage of being compatible with a large variety of metal ions like e.g. gallium, indium, yttrium, lutetium and copper [117]. DOTA is a stronger chelator than the open-chain DTPA in e.g. OctreoScan due to its macrocyclic structure, creating more stable complexes with the radioactive metal cation [123, 124]. This feature makes the chelator possible for use in various imaging and therapeutic applications.

Imaging with ^{68}Ga-Labelled Somatostatin Analogues

Standardized guidelines are now available for imaging using the three ^{68}Ga-labelled tracers DOTA-TOC, -TATE and -NOC. The radioactivity administered should be 100-200 MBq, and maximum 50 μg of the peptide. Activities below 100 MBq may give poor image quality [125]. The amount of radioactivity available for the scanning will depend on the age of the ^{68}Ge/^{68}Ga generator and number of patients scanned per day [77]. The acquisition in the scanner is started 1 h post-injection, and after 70 ± 20 min maximum tumour activity is observed in tumour [83]. Excretion of the tracer is almost exclusively through the kidneys [83]. When it comes to interpretation of images there is a risk of false positive findings in the pancreatic head having a large natural abundance of the SSTR [60, 126]. Another thing to take into consideration when interpreting images is the presence of inflammation, since SSTR is expressed on activated lymphocytes [77].

In SST imaging, the optimal tumour to non-tumour ratio is not obtained with the highest specific activity (ratio of radioactivity over amount of substance), as shown by several studies [127-129]. This result contradicts with results from many other PET imaging applications where a higher specific activity gives a higher contrast. The same phenomenon has however been observed also in e.g. bombesin [130], and antibody [131-133] tracer studies. Therefore the key is to find an optimal amount of peptide for both imaging and therapy. In the case of [^{68}Ga]DOTA-TOC 50 µg of peptide has been reported to give the highest tumour to non-tumour contrast [127].

Since SSTR is mainly found in well differentiated tumours and to less extent in poorly differentiated tumours SST imaging has prognostic value. Semi quantitative measurements like standardized uptake value (SUV) can be very helpful in staging and restaging [14].

The imaging using the ^{68}Ga-labelled octreotides includes [77]:

- Staging
- Restaging after surgery or therapy
- Localization of unknown primary tumour (CUP) with known secondary lesions
- Selection of patients suited for therapy with radioactive or non-radioactive SST compounds

In a recent comparison of cost it was concluded that a PET/CT scan with [^{68}Ga]DOTA-TOC was less expensive than SRS and SPECT/CT scans with OctreoScan in Germany, considering both material and personnel costs [134].

Comparative studies for ^{68}Ga-labelled DOTA-TOC, DOTA-TATE and DOTA-NOC have been performed with tracers and imaging techniques like OctreoScan, but also with CT, MRI, [^{18}F]FDG and [^{18}F]FDOPA PET.

Imaging with [^{68}Ga]DOTA-TOC

In 1997 the first reports on DOTA-TOC were published, in which the labelling was performed with ^{111}In or ^{90}Y [135-137]. From that on this compound has been extensively studied and the most attention has been received by [^{68}Ga]DOTA-TOC and its application in PET/CT NET imaging. A great number of clinical studies on [^{68}Ga]DOTA-TOC in NETs and also other applications have been reported [79, 83, 94, 138].

Henze et al reported an imaging study with [^{68}Ga]DOTA-TOC in patients with meningiomas where even lesions down to 7-8 mm diameter could be clearly visualized with high tracer uptake, whereas the lower limit in SPECT using OctreoScan is 2.7 cm [138]. Also Gehler et al [139] reported [^{68}Ga]DOTA-TOC to be highly useful in therapy planning in patients with meningiomas.

The ^{68}Ga tracer showed both higher sensitivity and tumour to non-tumour ratio compared to SRS, especially in detection of small lesions [83, 84] , and also when compared to CT and/or MRI [60, 140, 141]. One study concluded that [^{68}Ga]DOTA-TOC PET is superior to CT and conventional bone scintigraphy in the early detection and restaging of bone metastases in patients with NET [85]. Buchmann et al [94] reported that [^{68}Ga]DOTA-TOC was significantly better that OctreoScan in detection of NETs in bone, lung, liver and brain, and concluded that using [^{68}Ga]DOTA-TOC gives a great advantage in guiding of clinical management.

In one study including patients having SSTR positive tumours and metastases [^{68}Ga]DOTA-TOC PET identified 100% and OctreoScan SRS and SPECT only 85% of 40 predefined lesions. Tumour to non-tumour ratios were higher, kidney accumulation lower and >30% additional lesions were detected using [^{68}Ga]DOTA-TOC. The high tumour to non-tumour ratio was reached within 30-40 min post injection. This makes detection of very small lesions possible, which is important in staging, therapy planning and restaging after therapy. The tracer was shown to be stable in serum with no radioactive metabolites present after 4 h [83]. Also [^{68}Ga]DOTA-TOC was shown to be useful in selection of patients for treatment with [^{90}Y]DOTA-TOC, since only patients with a high SSTR density somatostatin analogue treatment can be performed [79].

The recently developed fused PET/MRI has great potential for further improvements of the usefulness of the PET technique [142, 143]. It has been implemented in the imaging of meningioma with [^{68}Ga]DOTA-TOC and the results indicated a more detailed volume delineation of meningiomas, compared to separate PET/CT and MRI. Using PET/MRI imaging reduces the number of different scans needed when the combinations of needed procedures can be reduced from CT, MRI, and PET/CT to only CT and PET/MRI [142].

Imaging with [^{68}Ga]DOTA-TATE

DOTA-TATE first occurred in literature in year 2000 [91, 144], when it was labelled with ^{64}Cu and ^{90}Y [144]. [^{68}Ga]DOTA-TATE has since then been used in a number of different imaging applications and compared to other tracers and imaging techniques.

In a study containing 25 patients with histologically proven metastatic GEP-NET, [^{68}Ga]DOTA-TATE had a sensitivity of 96% compared to 56% for [^{18}F]FDOPA [86]. [^{68}Ga]DOTA-TATE was used in a study consisting of patients with paraganglioma [145]. In this case CT and [^{123}I]MIBG (metaiodobenzylguanidine) imaging failed to recognize a reoccurring malignant abdominal paraganglioma [146]. The tracer [^{123}I]MIBG binds to catecholamine-secreting tumours (pheochromocytomas, paragangliomas and neuroblastomas) [14]. [^{68}Ga]DOTA-TATE on the other hand showed high uptake in the tumour. In cases where MIBG imaging is negative [^{68}Ga]DOTA-TATE PET should be considered, and if positive, therapy using [^{90}Y]DOTA-TATE is applicable [146, 147]. Naji et al [148] compared [^{68}Ga]DOTA-TATE and [^{123}I]MIBG in imaging of malignant neural crest tumours (NCT). They concluded that [^{68}Ga]DOTA-TATE is a better imaging agent for NCT and can detect significantly more lesions.

In a comparative study of [^{68}Ga]DOTA-TATE and [^{18}F]FDG the authors found that the ^{68}Ga tracer had great affinity for well differentiated NETs and that the ^{18}F tracer was good for imaging poorly differentiated NETs. A combination of the two tracers gave a sensitivity of 92% compared to 82% and 66% respectively when using [^{68}Ga]DOTA-TATE and [^{18}F]FDG alone in 38 patients with primary or recurrent NETs. The two tracers might therefore have a complementary role making the investigation of metastases more complete [78].

In a recent publication Hofman et al [149] claim that [^{68}Ga]DOTA-TATE PET/CT can replace OctreoScan SRS on the ground of its higher accuracy, faster acquisition, and lower radiation dose for both patients and personnel. Especially in patients with unknown primary tumour and very small lesions [^{68}Ga]DOTA-TATE is to prefer prior to surgery or in choosing PRRT.

[^{68}Ga]DOTA-TATE has been applied in other applications than NETs. In patients, having prior cardiovascular events and calcified atherosclerotic plaques there was an increased [^{68}Ga]DOTA-TATE uptake in the left anterior descending (LAD), showing that this tracer can have a role in imaging plaque in the coronary arteries [150].

In a comparative study including 20 GEP-NET patients, [68Ga]DOTA-NOC and [68Ga]DOTA-TATE had similar accuracy but [68Ga]DOTA-TATE higher lesion uptake [151]. When comparing [68Ga]DOTA-TOC and [68Ga]DOTA-TATE in 40 patients with metastatic NETs the results were highly comparable, even though DOTA-TATE has a 10-fold higher affinity for sst$_2$ [152].

An intra-individual comparison of [68Ga]DOTA-NOC and [68Ga]DOTA-TATE of a patient having metastases of a neuroendocrine pancreatic carcinoma showed that [68Ga]DOTA-NOC had a higher uptake in lesions compared to [68Ga]DOTA-TATE. Very small lesions were only detected using [68Ga]DOTA-NOC and not with [68Ga]DOTA-TATE. This was probably due to the affinity of DOTA-NOC to three of the receptor subtypes sst$_{2-3,5}$ compared to only sst$_2$ for DOTA-TATE. Also the internalisation is significantly higher for DOTA-NOC than for DOTA-TATE [90]. [68Ga]DOTA-TATE was confirmed as having a diagnostic role as an accurate method of identifying primary GEP-NET tumours and distant metastases [153].

Imaging with [68Ga]DOTA-NOC

In 2003 Wild et al introduced DOTA-NOC, having high affinity for the SST subtypes 2, 3 and 5 [92]. In 2005 the first PET/CT image using [68Ga]DOTA-NOC was published, showing high uptake in liver and bone metastases in a patient with advanced NET [154].

[68Ga]DOTA-NOC has been shown to be especially useful in imaging of NETs in unusual places in the body like kidney, prostate, ear, breast, uterus, ovary, and also paraganglioma. In the study by Fanti et al [68Ga]DOTA-NOC gave additional information when compared to conventional imaging in 7/14 cases, and the exam was clinically useful in 85% of the cases [89]. [68Ga]DOTA-NOC was reported to be more accurate when compared to [18F]FDOPA for detection of both primary tumour and secondary lesions in GEP-NET and lung, in a 13 patient study [88]. The easier preparation of a 68Ga-labelled peptide is also a clear advantage over the 18F-labelled compound.

[68Ga]DOTA-NOC imaging gives significantly higher sensitivity compared to OctreoScan especially for bone metastases, liver and small lymph node lesions [14]. It can also in many cases detect the primary tumour in patients with known metastases [14, 155]. The superiority of PET/CT imaging with [^{68}Ga]DOTA-NOC over OctreoScan has been shown in unknown primary neuroendocrine tumours (CUP-NET) [156]. Maximum standardized uptake value (SUV$_{max}$) correlates with the pathologic and clinical characteristics and SUV$_{max}$ was higher in patients having pancreatic endocrine tumours and also in those with well-differentiated carcinoma [157]. [^{68}Ga]DOTA-NOC has been reported to give a low radiation dose to organs in the body and primarily to kidney and urinary bladder wall as the excretion mainly is renal [158]. In a 90 patients NET study by Ambrosini et al [^{68}Ga]DOTA-NOC PET/CT affected either the staging or therapy in 50 of the patients. In the case of therapy most changes was introduction or continuation of PRRT [159].

[^{68}Ga]DOTA-NOC has been proven useful in other cases than NET like MTC [160]. Ambrosini et al reported the usefulness of [^{68}Ga]DOTA-NOC imaging in patients with idiopathic pulmonary fibrosis [161]. In an imaging study of carotid body chemodectomas (CBC) patients [^{68}Ga]DOTA-NOC was useful and previously unknown lesions could be detected with effect on patient treatment [162].

Somatostatin Analogues Labelled with Other PET Nuclides

Octreotide compounds have also been labelled with other PET nuclides [163]. DOTA-TOC labelled with ^{66}Ga (t$_{½}$ = 9.5 h) was prepared and preclinically evaluated with results comparable to [^{68}Ga]DOTA-TOC [28]. Gallium-66 however has the disadvantage of being cyclotron produced.

Various SST analogues have been labelled with ^{64}Cu (t$_{½}$ = 12.7 h), first by using the chelator TETA (1,4,8,11-tetraazacyclotetradecane-1,4,8,11-tetraacetic acid) [34-36]. In a study including eight NET patients [^{64}Cu]TETA-octreotide detected more lesions than OctreoScan in two cases and in one case OctreoScan detected more [34]. The complex between TETA and ^{64}Cu was reported to be unstable *in vivo* in the liver [35]. A new type of cross-bridged macrocyclic chelator, CB-TE2A (4,11-bis(carboxymethyl)-1,4,8,11-tetra-azabicyclo[6.6.2]hexadecane) was therefore introduced [164], and its complex with ^{64}Cu was shown to be more stable in rats compared to [^{64}Cu]TETA [165]. The highly stable chelator DOTA has also been used to label octreotide with ^{64}Cu. [^{64}Cu]DOTA-TOC was able to clearly image a SSTR positive tumour and seemed to be a potential PET tracer in the clinical phase [37]. [^{64}Cu]DOTA-TATE was recently investigated in a first-in-humans study and showed excellent imaging quality, reduced radiation burden, and increased lesion detection rate when compared with OctreoScan [38]. PEGylated liposomes labelled with ^{64}Cu through TATE conjugated to the surface has been shown to be a promising new imaging agent for GEP-NET imaging [39].

DOTA-TOC has been labelled with the cyclotron produced positron emitter ^{86}Y (t$_{1/2}$=14.7 h) and compared with OctreoScan in three patients having metastatic carcinoid tumours. The results showed that [^{86}Y]DOTA-TOC gave the most accurate images [31]. In a phase I PET study of 24 patients with SSTR positive GEP-NETs, [^{86}Y]DOTA-TOC gave accurate dosimetry of both tumour and kidneys [30].Yttrium-86 can be used in a theranostic pair with the β-emitting ^{90}Y.

The positron emitter ^{110m}In (t$_{1/2}$=69 min) was used in a one patient study where it was compared to the ^{111}In containing OctreoScan, and the result showed higher resolution and recovery for the ^{110m}In analogue [29].

Somatostatin analogues labelled with ^{18}F (t$_{1/2}$=110 min) can be prepared by using a ^{18}F containing prosthetic group. In a study of tumour bearing rats 2-[^{18}F]fluoropropionyl-D-Phe^1-octreotide [24, 25] had high affinity to SSTR, but not suitable pharmacokinetics. The high lipophilicity of the tracer lead to hepatobiliary excretion and this together with the low tumour to non-tumour ratio led to that the tracer was not further investigated [24]. To decrease the unfavourable high lipophilicity carbohydrated ^{18}F-labelled somatostatin analogues [166] was introduced. N^α-(1-Deoxy-D-fructosyl)-N^ε-(2-[^{18}F] fluoropropionyl)-Lys^0-Tyr^3-octreotate ([^{18}F]FP-Gluc-TOCA) showed high tumour uptake, good pharmacokinetics, and revealed in great detail multiple liver metastases [23]. In 2004 Schottelius et al [167] reported Cel-S-Dpr([^{18}F]FBOA)TOCA (cellobios-2,3-diaminopropionic acid(N-(4-[^{18}F] fluorobenzylidene)oxime) Tyr^3-octreotate) to be the first ^{18}F-labelled SST analogue suitable for routine use in the clinic. The two [^{18}F]fluoroethyl-triazole-Tyr^3-octreotate radioligands [^{18}F]FET-βAG-TOCA and [^{18}F]FET-G-TOCA have favourable stability, binding affinity, and pharmacokinetics for imaging sst$_2$ positive tumours at an early stage as shown in *in vitro* studies [26]. Recently NOTA conjugated octreotides have been labelled with ^{18}F by first creating the complex Al^{18}F, and then performing a labelling similar to ^{68}Ga-labelling [168, 169]. The drawback of using ^{18}F-labelled compounds for somatostatin imaging is that they are not possible to use as counterparts in a theranostic pair.

In 2004 Henriksen et al reported the synthesis of a ^{11}C-labelled octreotide, Cel-Dpr-[^{11}C]MBOA-TOCA [22]. Evaluation of the tracer in rat pancreas carcinoma xenografted mice showed high tumour to non-tumour ratio and suitable pharmacokinetics for imaging of SSTR overexpressing tumours.

Also [76]Br-labelled analogues have been prepared. The two compounds 4-[[76]Br]bromobenzoyl-octreotide and 5-[[76]Br]bromo-3-pyridinecarboxyoctreotide had high non-specific binding to meningioma in heart tissue and low affinity to SSTR [27]. DOTA-TOC has been labelled with the positron emitting [44]Sc ($t_{1/2}$=3.97 h). Scandium-44 is obtained from a [44]Ti/[44]Sc generator. The complex between DOTA and [44]Sc was highly stable and the tracer will be evaluated in preclinical and clinical studies. Scandium-44 can be used together with the β$^-$emitter [47]Sc for theranostics [32].

At this point, the three ^{68}Ga-labelled peptides DOTA-TATE, DOTA-TATE and DOTA-NOC are most promising of the somatostatin PET tracers.

CONCLUSION

Molecular imaging has the potential to greatly improve the outcome for NET patients by using personalized medicine. Early detection using highly sensitive and specific tracers will be the key to novel effective treatments of metastasizing neuroendocrine carcinomas. Somatostatin imaging is highly useful for diagnosis, therapy planning and follow-up after treatment. The use of ^{68}Ga-labelled DOTA-TOC, DOTA-TATE and DOTA-NOC in NET imaging is increasing all over the world. Many reports show the superiority of ^{68}Ga peptide PET/CT imaging over other tracers and techniques like SRS and morphological imaging. Not only is the specificity and sensitivity higher but the tracers in combination with the PET imaging technique can also quantify the SST expression presenting a non-invasive procedure for selecting patients suitable for somatostatin analogue treatment. The high spatial resolution of PET in combination with highly specific tracers allows detection of very small lesions. The synthesis of the ^{68}Ga-labelled peptides is convenient from a relatively inexpensive easy-to-handle [68]Ge/^{68}Ga-generator and the ^{68}Ga half-life of 68 min is compatible with the pharmacokinetics of the binding of the tracer to the receptor.

Today the three ^{68}Ga-labelled octreotides DOTA-TOC, DOTA-TATE and DOTA-NOC are in standard routine clinical diagnostic, and will in a close future replace the old golden standard Octreoscan. Especially the future more extensive use of PET/MRI will make ^{68}Ga PET even more useful in the clinic.

REFERENCES

[1] Oberg K. Neuroendocrine gastrointestinal tumours. Annals of oncology : *official Journal of the European Society for Medical Oncology / ESMO.* 1996;7(5):453-63. Epub 1996/07/01.

[2] Modlin IM, Oberg K, Chung DC, Jensen RT, de Herder WW, Thakker RV, et al. Gastroenteropancreatic neuroendocrine tumours. *The lancet oncology.* 2008;9(1):61-72. Epub 2008/01/08.

[3] Modlin IM, Lye KD, Kidd M. A 5-decade analysis of 13,715 carcinoid tumors. *Cancer.* 2003;97(4):934-59. Epub 2003/02/06.

[4] Modlin IM, Kidd M, Latich I, Zikusoka MN, Shapiro MD. Current status of gastrointestinal carcinoids. *Gastroenterology.* 2005; 128(6): 1717-51. Epub 2005/05/12.

[5] Norton JA, Warren RS, Kelly MG, Zuraek MB, Jensen RT. Aggressive surgery for metastatic liver neuroendocrine tumors. *Surgery.* 2003; 134(6): 1057-63; discussion 63-5. Epub 2003/12/12.

[6] Sundin A, Garske U, Orlefors H. Nuclear imaging of neuroendocrine tumours. *Best practice and research Clinical endocrinology and metabolism.* 2007;21(1):69-85. Epub 2007/03/27.

[7] Ramage JK, Davies AH, Ardill J, Bax N, Caplin M, Grossman A, et al. Guidelines for the management of gastroenteropancreatic neuroendocrine (including carcinoid) tumours. *Gut.* 2005;54 Suppl 4:iv1-16. Epub 2005/05/13.

[8] Reichlin S. Somatostatin: historical aspects. *Scandinavian Journal of gastroenterology Supplement.* 1986;119:1-10. Epub 1986/01/01.

[9] Krenning EP, Kwekkeboom DJ, Bakker WH, Breeman WA, Kooij PP, Oei HY, et al. Somatostatin receptor scintigraphy with [111In-DTPA-D-Phe1]- and [123I-Tyr3]-octreotide: the Rotterdam experience with more than 1000 patients. *European Journal of Nuclear Medicine.* 1993;20(8): 716-31. Epub 1993/08/01.

[10] Guillermet-Guibert J, Lahlou H, Pyronnet S, Bousquet C, Susini C. Endocrine tumours of the gastrointestinal tract. Somatostatin receptors as tools for diagnosis and therapy: molecular aspects. *Best practice and research Clinical gastroenterology.*2005;19(4):535-51.Epub 2005/09/27.

[11] Guillemin R. Hypothalamic hormones a.k.a. hypothalamic releasing factors. *The Journal of endocrinology.* 2005;184(1):11-28. Epub 2005/01/12.

[12] Cescato R, Schulz S, Waser B, Eltschinger V, Rivier JE, Wester HJ, et al. Internalization of sst2, sst3, and sst5 receptors: effects of somatostatin

agonists and antagonists. *Journal of Nuclear Medicine*: official publication, Society of Nuclear Medicine. 2006;47(3):502-11. Epub 2006/03/04.

[13] Reubi JC, Waser B. Concomitant expression of several peptide receptors in neuroendocrine tumours: molecular basis for in vivo multireceptor tumour targeting. *European Journal of Nuclear Medicine and Molecular Imaging*. 2003;30(5):781-93. Epub 2003/04/23.

[14] Rufini V, Calcagni ML, Baum RP. Imaging of neuroendocrine tumors. *Seminars in nuclear medicine*. 2006;36(3):228-47. Epub 2006/06/10.

[15] Oberg KE, Reubi JC, Kwekkeboom DJ, Krenning EP. Role of somatostatins in gastroenteropancreatic neuroendocrine tumor development and therapy. *Gastroenterology*. 2010;139(3):742-53, 53 e1. Epub 2010/07/20.

[16] Waldherr C, Pless M, Maecke HR, Schumacher T, Crazzolara A, Nitzsche EU, et al. Tumor response and clinical benefit in neuroendocrine tumors after 7.4 GBq (90)Y-DOTATOC. *Journal of Nuclear Medicine:* official publication, Society of Nuclear Medicine. 2002;43(5):610-6. Epub 2002/05/08.

[17] Oberg K. Gallium-68 somatostatin receptor PET/CT: Is it time to replace (111)Indium DTPA octreotide for patients with neuroendocrine tumors? *Endocrine*. 2012;42(1):3-4. Epub 2012/05/09.

[18] Lamberts SW, Bakker WH, Reubi JC, Krenning EP. Somatostatin-receptor imaging in the localization of endocrine tumors. *The New England Journal of medicine*. 1990;323(18):1246-9. Epub 1990/11/01.

[19] Gabriel M, Decristoforo C, Donnemiller E, Ulmer H, Watfah Rychlinski C, Mather SJ, et al. An intrapatient comparison of 99mTc-EDDA/HYNIC-TOC with 111In-DTPA-octreotide for diagnosis of somatostatin receptor-expressing tumors. *Journal of Nuclear Medicine:* official publication, Society of Nuclear Medicine. 2003;44(5):708-16. Epub 2003/05/07.

[20] Decristoforo C, Mather SJ, Cholewinski W, Donnemiller E, Riccabona G, Moncayo R. 99mTc-EDDA/HYNIC-TOC: a new 99mTc-labelled radiopharmaceutical for imaging somatostatin receptor-positive tumours; first clinical results and intra-patient comparison with 111In-labelled octreotide derivatives. *European Journal of Nuclear Medicine*. 2000; 27(9): 1318-25. Epub 2000/09/28.

[21] Smith-Jones PM, Stolz B, Bruns C, Albert R, Reist HW, Fridrich R, et al. Gallium-67/gallium-68-[DFO]-octreotide--a potential radio-

pharmaceutical for PET imaging of somatostatin receptor-positive tumors: synthesis and radiolabeling in vitro and preliminary in vivo studies. *Journal of Nuclear Medicine*: official publication, Society of Nuclear Medicine. 1994;35(2):317-25. Epub 1994/02/01.

[22] Henriksen G, Schottelius M, Poethko T, Hauser A, Wolf I, Schwaiger M, et al. Proof of principle for the use of 11C-labelled peptides in tumour diagnosis with PET. *European Journal of Nuclear Medicine and Molecular Imaging*. 2004;31(12):1653-7. Epub 2004/08/17.

[23] Wester HJ, Schottelius M, Scheidhauer K, Meisetschlager G, Herz M, Rau FC, et al. PET imaging of somatostatin receptors: design, synthesis and preclinical evaluation of a novel 18F-labelled, carbohydrated analogue of octreotide. *European Journal of Nuclear Medicine and Molecular Imaging*. 2003;30(1):117-22. Epub 2002/12/17.

[24] Wester HJ, Brockmann J, Rosch F, Wutz W, Herzog H, Smith-Jones P, et al. PET-pharmacokinetics of 18F-octreotide: a comparison with 67Ga-DFO- and 86Y-DTPA-octreotide. *Nuclear Medicine and Biology*. 1997; 24(4):275-86. Epub 1997/05/01.

[25] Guhlke S, Wester HJ, Bruns C, Stocklin G. (2-[18F]fluoropropionyl-(D)phe1)-octreotide, a potential radiopharmaceutical for quantitative somatostatin receptor imaging with PET: synthesis, radiolabeling, in vitro validation and biodistribution in mice. *Nuclear Medicine and Biology*. 1994;21(6):819-25. Epub 1994/08/01.

[26] Leyton J, Iddon L, Perumal M, Indrevoll B, Glaser M, Robins E, et al. Targeting somatostatin receptors: preclinical evaluation of novel 18F-fluoroethyltriazole-Tyr3-octreotate analogs for PET. *Journal of Nuclear Medicine:* official publication, Society of Nuclear Medicine. 2011; 52(9): 1441-8. Epub 2011/08/20.

[27] Yngve U, Khan TS, Bergstrom M, Langstrom B. Labelling of octreotide using 76Br-prosthetic groups. *J. Labelled Cpd. Radiopharm*. 2001;44: 561-73.

[28] Ugur O, Kothari PJ, Finn RD, Zanzonico P, Ruan S, Guenther I, et al. Ga-66 labeled somatostatin analogue DOTA-DPhe1-Tyr3-octreotide as a potential agent for positron emission tomography imaging and receptor mediated internal radiotherapy of somatostatin receptor positive tumors. *Nuclear medicine and biology*. 2002;29(2):147-57. Epub 2002/02/02.

[29] Lubberink M, Tolmachev V, Widstrom C, Bruskin A, Lundqvist H, Westlin JE. 110mIn-DTPA-D-Phe1-octreotide for imaging of neuroendocrine tumors with PET. *Journal of Nuclear Medicine* : official

publication, Society of Nuclear Medicine. 2002;43(10):1391-7. Epub 2002/10/09.

[30] Jamar F, Barone R, Mathieu I, Walrand S, Labar D, Carlier P, et al. 86Y-DOTA0)-D-Phe1-Tyr3-octreotide (SMT487)--a phase 1 clinical study: pharmacokinetics, biodistribution and renal protective effect of different regimens of amino acid co-infusion. *European Journal of Nuclear Medicine and Molecular Imaging.* 2003;30(4):510-8. Epub 2003/02/13.

[31] Forster GJ, Engelbach MJ, Brockmann JJ, Reber HJ, Buchholz HG, Macke HR, et al. Preliminary data on biodistribution and dosimetry for therapy planning of somatostatin receptor positive tumours: comparison of (86)Y-DOTATOC and (111)In-DTPA-octreotide. *European Journal of Nuclear Medicine.* 2001;28(12):1743-50. Epub 2001/12/06.

[32] Pruszynski M, Majkowska-Pilip A, Loktionova NS, Eppard E, Roesch F. Radiolabeling of DOTATOC with the long-lived positron emitter 44Sc. *Applied radiation and isotopes : including data, instrumentation and methods for use in agriculture, industry and medicine.* 2012; 70(6):974-9. Epub 2012/04/03.

[33] Sprague JE, Peng Y, Sun X, Weisman GR, Wong EH, Achilefu S, et al. Preparation and biological evaluation of copper-64-labeled tyr3-octreotate using a cross-bridged macrocyclic chelator. *Clinical cancer research : an official Journal of the American Association for Cancer Research.* 2004;10(24):8674-82. Epub 2004/12/30.

[34] Anderson CJ, Dehdashti F, Cutler PD, Schwarz SW, Laforest R, Bass LA, et al. 64Cu-TETA-octreotide as a PET imaging agent for patients with neuroendocrine tumors. *Journal of Nuclear Medicine:* official publication, Society of Nuclear Medicine. 2001;42(2):213-21. Epub 2001/02/24.

[35] Bass LA, Wang M, Welch MJ, Anderson CJ. In vivo transchelation of copper-64 from TETA-octreotide to superoxide dismutase in rat liver. *Bioconjugate Chemistry.* 2000;11(4):527-32. Epub 2000/07/18.

[36] Lewis JS, Lewis MR, Srinivasan A, Schmidt MA, Wang J, Anderson CJ. Comparison of four 64Cu-labeled somatostatin analogues in vitro and in a tumor-bearing rat model: evaluation of new derivatives for positron emission tomography imaging and targeted radiotherapy. *Journal of Medicinal Chemistry.* 1999;42(8):1341-7. Epub 1999/04/23.

[37] Hanaoka H, Tominaga H, Yamada K, Paudyal P, Iida Y, Watanabe S, et al. Evaluation of (64)Cu-labeled DOTA-D-Phe(1)-Tyr (3)-octreotide ((64)Cu-DOTA-TOC) for imaging somatostatin receptor-expressing

tumors. *Annals of Nuclear Medicine.* 2009;23(6):559-67. Epub 2009/06/09.

[38] Pfeifer A, Knigge U, Mortensen J, Oturai P, Berthelsen AK, Loft A, et al. Clinical PET of Neuroendocrine Tumors Using 64Cu-DOTATATE: First-in-Humans Study. *Journal of Nuclear Medicine*: official publication, Society of Nuclear Medicine. 2012. Epub 2012/07/12.

[39] Petersen AL, Binderup T, Jolck RI, Rasmussen P, Henriksen JR, Pfeifer AK, et al. Positron emission tomography evaluation of somatostatin receptor targeted 64Cu-TATE-liposomes in a human neuroendocrine carcinoma mouse model. Journal of controlled release : *Official Journal of the Controlled Release Society.* 2012;160(2):254-63. Epub 2012/01/17.

[40] Otte A, Mueller-Brand J, Dellas S, Nitzsche EU, Herrmann R, Maecke HR. Yttrium-90-labelled somatostatin-analogue for cancer treatment. *Lancet.* 1998;351(9100):417-8. Epub 1998/03/03.

[41] Bodei L, Cremonesi M, Zoboli S, Grana C, Bartolomei M, Rocca P, et al. Receptor-mediated radionuclide therapy with 90Y-DOTATOC in association with amino acid infusion: a phase I study. *European Journal of Nuclear Medicine and Molecular Imaging.* 2003;30(2):207-16. Epub 2003/01/29.

[42] de Jong M, Breeman WA, Bernard BF, Bakker WH, Schaar M, van Gameren A, et al. [177Lu-DOTA(0),Tyr3] octreotate for somatostatin receptor-targeted radionuclide therapy. *International Journal of Cancer Journal International Du Cancer.* 2001;92(5):628-33. Epub 2001/05/08.

[43] Norenberg JP, Krenning BJ, Konings IR, Kusewitt DF, Nayak TK, Anderson TL, et al. 213Bi-[DOTA0, Tyr3]octreotide peptide receptor radionuclide therapy of pancreatic tumors in a preclinical animal model. Clinical cancer research : *an Official Journal of the American Association for Cancer Research.* 2006;12(3 Pt 1):897-903. Epub 2006/02/10.

[44] Krenning EP, Bakker WH, Breeman WA, Koper JW, Kooij PP, Ausema L, et al. Localisation of endocrine-related tumours with radioiodinated analogue of somatostatin. *Lancet.* 1989;1(8632):242-4. Epub 1989/02/04.

[45] Lamberts SW, Reubi JC, Bakker WH, Krenning EP. Somatostatin receptor imaging with 123I-Tyr3-Octreotide. *Zeitschrift fur Gastroenterologie.* 1990;28 Suppl 2:20-1. Epub 1990/09/01.

[46] Okarvi SM. Peptide-based radiopharmaceuticals: future tools for diagnostic imaging of cancers and other diseases. *Medicinal research reviews*. 2004;24(3):357-97. Epub 2004/03/03.

[47] Bakker WH, Albert R, Bruns C, Breeman WA, Hofland LJ, Marbach P, et al. [111In-DTPA-D-Phe1]-octreotide, a potential radiopharmaceutical for imaging of somatostatin receptor-positive tumors: synthesis, radiolabeling and in vitro validation. *Life sciences*. 1991;49(22):1583-91. Epub 1991/01/01.

[48] Bakker WH, Krenning EP, Reubi JC, Breeman WA, Setyono-Han B, de Jong M, et al. In vivo application of [111In-DTPA-D-Phe1]-octreotide for detection of somatostatin receptor-positive tumors in rats. *Life sciences*. 1991;49(22):1593-601. Epub 1991/01/01.

[49] Macke HR, Smith-Jones P, Maina T, Stolz B, Albert R, Bruns C, et al. New octreotide derivatives for in vivo targeting of somatostatin receptor-positive tumors for single photon emission computed tomography (SPECT) and positron emission tomography (PET). *Hormone and metabolic research Supplement series*. 1993;27:12-7. Epub 1993/01/01.

[50] Rambaldi PF, Cuccurullo V, Briganti V, Mansi L. The present and future role of (111)In pentetreotide in the PET era. *Q. J. Nucl. Med. Mol. Imaging*. 2005;49(3):225-35. Epub 2005/09/21.

[51] Marienhagen J, Schalke B, Aebert H, Held P, Eilles C, Bogdahn U. Somatostatin receptor scintigraphy in thymoma imaging method and clinical application. *Pathology, research and practice*. 1999;195(8):575-81. Epub 1999/09/14.

[52] Lebtahi R, Cadiot G, Sarda L, Daou D, Faraggi M, Petegnief Y, et al. Clinical impact of somatostatin receptor scintigraphy in the management of patients with neuroendocrine gastroenteropancreatic tumors. *Journal of nuclear medicine:* official publication, Society of Nuclear Medicine. 1997;38(6):853-8. Epub 1997/06/01.

[53] Pepe G, Moncayo R, Bombardieri E, Chiti A. Somatostatin receptor SPECT. *European Journal of Nuclear Medicine and Molecular Imaging*. 2012;39 Suppl 1:S41-51. Epub 2012/03/06.

[54] Ingui CJ, Shah NP, Oates ME. Endocrine neoplasm scintigraphy: added value of fusing SPECT/CT images compared with traditional side-by-side analysis. *Clinical nuclear medicine*. 2006;31(11):665-72. Epub 2006/10/21.

[55] Hillel PG, van Beek EJ, Taylor C, Lorenz E, Bax ND, Prakash V, et al. The clinical impact of a combined gamma camera/CT imaging system

on somatostatin receptor imaging of neuroendocrine tumours. *Clinical radiology*. 2006;61(7):579-87. Epub 2006/06/21.

[56] Cotton FA, Wilkinson G. *Advanced Inorganic Chemistry*. 5th ed. New York: Interscience; 1988.

[57] Kaltsas GA, Mukherjee JJ, Grossman AB. The value of radiolabelled MIBG and octreotide in the diagnosis and management of neuroendocrine tumours. Annals of oncology : *official Journal of the European Society for Medical Oncology / ESMO*. 2001;12 Suppl 2:S47-50. Epub 2002/01/05.

[58] Kaltsas G, Rockall A, Papadogias D, Reznek R, Grossman AB. Recent advances in radiological and radionuclide imaging and therapy of neuroendocrine tumours. *European journal of Endocrinology / European Federation of Endocrine Societies*. 2004;151(1):15-27. Epub 2004/07/14.

[59] Dromain C, de Baere T, Lumbroso J, Caillet H, Laplanche A, Boige V, et al. Detection of liver metastases from endocrine tumors: a prospective comparison of somatostatin receptor scintigraphy, computed tomography, and magnetic resonance imaging. *Journal of clinical oncology : Official Journal of the American Society of Clinical Oncology*. 2005;23(1):70-8. Epub 2004/12/31.

[60] Gabriel M, Decristoforo C, Kendler D, Dobrozemsky G, Heute D, Uprimny C, et al. 68Ga-DOTA-Tyr3-octreotide PET in neuroendocrine tumors: comparison with somatostatin receptor scintigraphy and CT. *Journal of Nuclear Medicine* : official publication, Society of Nuclear Medicine. 2007;48(4):508-18. Epub 2007/04/03.

[61] Oberg K, Kvols L, Caplin M, Delle Fave G, de Herder W, Rindi G, et al. Consensus report on the use of somatostatin analogs for the management of neuroendocrine tumors of the gastroenteropancreatic system. *Annals of oncology : Official Journal of the European Society for Medical Oncology / ESMO*. 2004;15(6):966-73. Epub 2004/05/21.

[62] Kwekkeboom DJ, Kam BL, van Essen M, Teunissen JJ, van Eijck CH, Valkema R, et al. Somatostatin-receptor-based imaging and therapy of gastroenteropancreatic neuroendocrine tumors. *Endocrine-related cancer*. 2010;17(1):R53-73. Epub 2009/12/10.

[63] Gibril F, Reynolds JC, Chen CC, Yu F, Goebel SU, Serrano J, et al. Specificity of somatostatin receptor scintigraphy: a prospective study and effects of false-positive localizations on management in patients with gastrinomas. *Journal of Nuclear Medicine*: official publication, Society of Nuclear Medicine. 1999;40(4):539-53. Epub 1999/04/21.

[64] van Eijck CH, de Jong M, Breeman WA, Slooter GD, Marquet RL, Krenning EP. Somatostatin receptor imaging and therapy of pancreatic endocrine tumors. *Annals of oncology : Official Journal of the European Society for Medical Oncology / ESMO*. 1999;10 Suppl 4:177-81. Epub 1999/08/07.

[65] Lim PS, Kim SM, Andrews DW, Intenzo CM, Corn BW, Curran WJJ. Somatostatin Receptor Imaging: Monitoring Tumor Response in Patients with Meningioma. *Acad. Radiol.* 1999:651.

[66] Chiti A, Savelli G, Fanti S, Bellanova B, Resnik N, Romeo A, et al. Somatostatin receptor imaging in neuroendocrine tumors. Biomedicine and pharmacotherapy = *Biomedecine and pharmacotherapie*. 1996; 50:409.

[67] Ambrosini V, Fani M, Fanti S, Forrer F, Maecke HR. Radiopeptide imaging and therapy in Europe. *Journal of Nuclear Medicine : official publication, Society of Nuclear Medicine*. 2011;52 Suppl 2:42S-55S. Epub 2011/12/22.

[68] Reubi JC, Lamberts SJ, Krenning EP. Receptor imaging of human diseases using radiolabeled peptides. *Journal of Receptor and Signal Transduction Research*. 1995;15(1-4):379-92. Epub 1995/01/01.

[69] Moncayo VM, Martin DR, Sarmiento JM, Zbytek B, Fox T, Schuster DM. (1)(1)(1)In OctreoScan SPECT-MRI fusion for the detection of a pancreatic insulinoma. *Clinical nuclear medicine*. 2012;37(3):e53-6. Epub 2012/02/09.

[70] *Principles of Nuclear Medicine*. Philadelphia: W.B. Saunders Company; 1995.

[71] *Positron Emission Tomography: Basic Science and Clinical Practise*. London: Springer-Verlag; 2003.

[72] Lodge MA, Braess H, Mahmoud F, Suh J, Englar N, Geyser-Stoops S, et al. Developments in nuclear cardiology: transition from single photon emission computed tomography to positron emission tomography-computed tomography. *The Journal of Invasive Cardiology*. 2005;17(9): 491-6. Epub 2005/09/08.

[73] Martin WH, Delbeke D, Patton JA, Sandler MP. Detection of malignancies with SPECT versus PET, with 2-[fluorine-18]fluoro-2-deoxy-D-glucose. *Radiology*. 1996;198(1):225-31. Epub 1996/01/01.

[74] Hartmann H, Zophel K, Freudenberg R, Oehme L, Andreeff M, Wunderlich G, et al. [Radiation exposure of patients during 68Ga-DOTATOC PET/CT examinations]. *Nuklearmedizin Nuclear medicine*.

2009;48(5):201-7. Epub 2009/07/30. Strahlenexposition der Patienten bei Untersuchungen mit 68Ga-DOTATOC am PET/CT.

[75] Adams S, Baum R, Rink T, Schumm-Drager PM, Usadel KH, Hor G. Limited value of fluorine-18 fluorodeoxyglucose positron emission tomography for the imaging of neuroendocrine tumours. *European Journal of Nuclear Medicine.* 1998;25(1):79-83. Epub 1998/03/07.

[76] Pasquali C, Rubello D, Sperti C, Gasparoni P, Liessi G, Chierichetti F, et al. Neuroendocrine tumor imaging: can 18F-fluorodeoxyglucose positron emission tomography detect tumors with poor prognosis and aggressive behavior? *World Journal of Surgery.* 1998;22(6):588-92. Epub 1998/05/23.

[77] Ambrosini V, Campana D, Tomassetti P, Fanti S. (6)(8)Ga-labelled peptides for diagnosis of gastroenteropancreatic NET. *European Journal of Nuclear Medicine and Molecular Imaging.* 2012;39 Suppl 1:S52-60. Epub 2012/03/06.

[78] Kayani I, Bomanji JB, Groves A, Conway G, Gacinovic S, Win T, et al. Functional imaging of neuroendocrine tumors with combined PET/CT using 68Ga-DOTATATE (DOTA-DPhe1,Tyr3-octreotate) and 18F-FDG. *Cancer.* 2008;112(11):2447-55. Epub 2008/04/03.

[79] Koukouraki S, Strauss LG, Georgoulias V, Eisenhut M, Haberkorn U, Dimitrakopoulou-Strauss A. Comparison of the pharmacokinetics of 68Ga-DOTATOC and [18F]FDG in patients with metastatic neuroendocrine tumours scheduled for 90Y-DOTATOC therapy. *European Journal of Nuclear Medicine and Molecular Imaging.* 2006;33(10):1115-22. Epub 2006/06/10.

[80] Schoder H, Yeung HW. Positron emission imaging of head and neck cancer, including thyroid carcinoma. *Seminars in nuclear medicine.* 2004; 34(3):180-97. Epub 2004/06/18.

[81] Freudenberg LS, Antoch G, Jentzen W, Pink R, Knust J, Gorges R, et al. Value of (124)I-PET/CT in staging of patients with differentiated thyroid cancer. *European radiology.* 2004;14(11):2092-8. Epub 2004/07/03.

[82] Lind P, Kohlfurst S. Respective roles of thyroglobulin, radioiodine imaging, and positron emission tomography in the assessment of thyroid cancer. *Seminars in nuclear medicine.* 2006;36(3):194-205. Epub 2006/06/10.

[83] Hofmann M, Maecke H, Borner R, Weckesser E, Schoffski P, Oei L, et al. Biokinetics and imaging with the somatostatin receptor PET

radioligand (68)Ga-DOTATOC: preliminary data. *European Journal of Nuclear Medicine.* 2001;28(12):1751-7. Epub 2001/12/06.

[84] Kowalski J, Henze M, Schuhmacher J, Macke HR, Hofmann M, Haberkorn U. Evaluation of positron emission tomography imaging using [68Ga]-DOTA-D Phe(1)-Tyr(3)-Octreotide in comparison to [111In]-DTPAOC SPECT. First results in patients with neuroendocrine tumors. *Molecular imaging and biology : MIB : the official publication of the Academy of Molecular Imaging.* 2003;5(1):42-8. Epub 2003/09/23.

[85] Putzer D, Gabriel M, Henninger B, Kendler D, Uprimny C, Dobrozemsky G, et al. Bone metastases in patients with neuroendocrine tumor: 68Ga-DOTA-Tyr3-octreotide PET in comparison to CT and bone scintigraphy. *Journal of Nuclear Medicine :* official publication, Society of Nuclear Medicine. 2009;50(8):1214-21. Epub 2009/07/21.

[86] Haug A, Auernhammer CJ, Wangler B, Tiling R, Schmidt G, Goke B, et al. Intraindividual comparison of 68Ga-DOTA-TATE and 18F-DOPA PET in patients with well-differentiated metastatic neuroendocrine tumours. *European Journal of Nuclear Medicine and Molecular Imaging.* 2009;36(5):765-70. Epub 2009/01/13.

[87] Srirajaskanthan R, Kayani I, Quigley AM, Soh J, Caplin ME, Bomanji J. The role of 68Ga-DOTATATE PET in patients with neuroendocrine tumors and negative or equivocal findings on 111In-DTPA-octreotide scintigraphy. *Journal of Nuclear Medicine :* official publication, Society of Nuclear Medicine. 2010;51(6):875-82. Epub 2010/05/21.

[88] Ambrosini V, Tomassetti P, Castellucci P, Campana D, Montini G, Rubello D, et al. Comparison between 68Ga-DOTA-NOC and 18F-DOPA PET for the detection of gastro-entero-pancreatic and lung neuro-endocrine tumours. *European Journal of Nuclear Medicine and Molecular Imaging.* 2008;35(8):1431-8. Epub 2008/04/18.

[89] Fanti S, Ambrosini V, Tomassetti P, Castellucci P, Montini G, Allegri V, et al. Evaluation of unusual neuroendocrine tumours by means of 68Ga-DOTA-NOC PET. Biomedicine and pharmacotherapy = *Biomedecine and pharmacotherapie.* 2008;62(10):667-71. Epub 2008/03/25.

[90] Antunes P, Ginj M, Zhang H, Waser B, Baum RP, Reubi JC, et al. Are radiogallium-labelled DOTA-conjugated somatostatin analogues superior to those labelled with other radiometals? *European Journal of Nuclear Medicine and Molecular Imaging.* 2007;34(7):982-93. Epub 2007/01/17.

[91] Reubi JC, Schar JC, Waser B, Wenger S, Heppeler A, Schmitt JS, et al. Affinity profiles for human somatostatin receptor subtypes SST1-SST5 of somatostatin radiotracers selected for scintigraphic and radiotherapeutic use. *European Journal of Nuclear Medicine.* 2000; 27(3): 273-82. Epub 2000/04/25.

[92] Wild D, Schmitt JS, Ginj M, Macke HR, Bernard BF, Krenning E, et al. DOTA-NOC, a high-affinity ligand of somatostatin receptor subtypes 2, 3 and 5 for labelling with various radiometals. *European Journal of Nuclear Medicine and Molecular Imaging.* 2003;30(10):1338-47. Epub 2003/08/26.

[93] Haug AR, Rominger A, Mustafa M, Auernhammer C, Goke B, Schmidt GP, et al. Treatment with octreotide does not reduce tumor uptake of (68)Ga-DOTATATE as measured by PET/CT in patients with neuroendocrine tumors. *Journal of Nuclear Medicine*: official publication, Society of Nuclear Medicine. 2011;52(11):1679-83. Epub 2011/10/07.

[94] Buchmann I, Henze M, Engelbrecht S, Eisenhut M, Runz A, Schafer M, et al. Comparison of 68Ga-DOTATOC PET and 111In-DTPAOC (Octreoscan) SPECT in patients with neuroendocrine tumours. *European Journal of Nuclear Medicine and Molecular Imaging.* 2007;34(10): 1617-26. Epub 2007/05/24.

[95] Heppeler A, Froidevaux S, Eberle AN, Maecke HR. Receptor targeting for tumor localisation and therapy with radiopeptides. *Current medicinal chemistry.* 2000;7(9):971-94. Epub 2000/07/27.

[96] Metz DC, Jensen RT. Gastrointestinal neuroendocrine tumors: pancreatic endocrine tumors. *Gastroenterology.* 2008;135(5):1469-92. Epub 2008/08/16.

[97] Virgolini I, Traub T, Novotny C, Leimer M, Fuger B, Li SR, et al. Experience with indium-111 and yttrium-90-labeled somatostatin analogs. *Current pharmaceutical design.* 2002;8(20):1781-807. Epub 2002/08/13.

[98] Forrer F, Valkema R, Kwekkeboom DJ, de Jong M, Krenning EP. Neuroendocrine tumors. Peptide receptor radionuclide therapy. *Best practice and research Clinical endocrinology and metabolism.* 2007; 21(1):111-29. Epub 2007/03/27.

[99] Kwekkeboom DJ, Teunissen JJ, Kam BL, Valkema R, de Herder WW, Krenning EP. Treatment of patients who have endocrine gastroenteropancreatic tumors with radiolabeled somatostatin analogues.

Hematology/oncology clinics of North America. 2007;21(3):561-73; x. Epub 2007/06/06.

[100] Lee DY, Li KC. Molecular theranostics: a primer for the imaging professional. *AJR American Journal of Roentgenology.* 2011;197(2): 318-24. Epub 2011/07/26.

[101] Jamar F, Fiasse R, Leners N, Pauwels S. Somatostatin receptor imaging with indium-111-pentetreotide in gastroenteropancreatic neuroendocrine tumors: safety, efficacy and impact on patient management. *Journal of Nuclear Medicine:* official publication, Society of Nuclear Medicine. 1995;36(4):542-9. Epub 1995/04/01.

[102] Kaltsas GA, Papadogias D, Makras P, Grossman AB. Treatment of advanced neuroendocrine tumours with radiolabelled somatostatin analogues. *Endocrine-related cancer.* 2005;12(4):683-99. Epub 2005/12/03.

[103] Kwekkeboom DJ, Teunissen JJ, Bakker WH, Kooij PP, de Herder WW, Feelders RA, et al. Radiolabeled somatostatin analog [177Lu-DOTA0,Tyr3]octreotate in patients with endocrine gastroentero-pancreatic tumors. *Journal of Clinical Oncology : Official Journal of the American Society of Clinical Oncology.* 2005;23(12): 2754-62. Epub 2005/04/20.

[104] Imhof A, Brunner P, Marincek N, Briel M, Schindler C, Rasch H, et al. Response, survival, and long-term toxicity after therapy with the radiolabeled somatostatin analogue [90Y-DOTA]-TOC in metastasized neuroendocrine cancers. *Journal of Clinical Oncology : Official Journal of the American Society of Clinical Oncology.* 2011;29(17):2416-23. Epub 2011/05/11.

[105] Bodei L, Cremonesi M, Grana C, Rocca P, Bartolomei M, Chinol M, et al. Receptor radionuclide therapy with 90Y-[DOTA]0-Tyr3-octreotide (90Y-DOTATOC) in neuroendocrine tumours. *European Journal of Nuclear Medicine and Molecular Imaging.* 2004;31(7):1038-46. Epub 2004/05/20.

[106] Valkema R, Pauwels S, Kvols LK, Barone R, Jamar F, Bakker WH, et al. Survival and response after peptide receptor radionuclide therapy with [90Y-DOTA0,Tyr3]octreotide in patients with advanced gastroenteropancreatic neuroendocrine tumors. *Seminars in nuclear medicine.* 2006;36(2):147-56. Epub 2006/03/07.

[107] Kwekkeboom DJ, Bakker WH, Kooij PP, Konijnenberg MW, Srinivasan A, Erion JL, et al. [177Lu-DOTAOTyr3]octreotate: comparison with

[111In-DTPAo]octreotide in patients. *European Journal of Nuclear Medicine.* 2001;28(9):1319-25. Epub 2001/10/05.

[108] Kwekkeboom DJ, de Herder WW, Kam BL, van Eijck CH, van Essen M, Kooij PP, et al. Treatment with the radiolabeled somatostatin analog [177 Lu-DOTA 0,Tyr3]octreotate: toxicity, efficacy, and survival. *Journal of Clinical Oncology : Official Journal of the American Society of Clinical Oncology.* 2008;26(13):2124-30. Epub 2008/05/01.

[109] van Essen M, Krenning EP, Bakker WH, de Herder WW, van Aken MO, Kwekkeboom DJ. Peptide receptor radionuclide therapy with 177Lu-octreotide in patients with foregut carcinoid tumours of bronchial, gastric and thymic origin. *European Journal of Nuclear Medicine and Molecular Imaging.* 2007;34(8):1219-27. Epub 2007/01/30.

[110] Van Essen M, Krenning EP, De Jong M, Valkema R, Kwekkeboom DJ. Peptide Receptor Radionuclide Therapy with radiolabelled somatostatin analogues in patients with somatostatin receptor positive tumours. *Acta Oncol.* 2007;46(6):723-34. Epub 2007/07/27.

[111] de Jong M, Breeman WA, Valkema R, Bernard BF, Krenning EP. Combination radionuclide therapy using 177Lu- and 90Y-labeled somatostatin analogs. *Journal of Nuclear Medicine*: official publication, Society of Nuclear Medicine. 2005;46 Suppl 1:13S-7S. Epub 2005/01/18.

[112] Ezziddin S, Lohmar J, Yong-Hing CJ, Sabet A, Ahmadzadehfar H, Kukuk G, et al. Does the pretherapeutic tumor SUV in 68Ga DOTATOC PET predict the absorbed dose of 177Lu octreotate? *Clinical nuclear medicine.* 2012;37(6):e141-7. Epub 2012/05/23.

[113] Haug AR, Auernhammer CJ, Wangler B, Schmidt GP, Uebleis C, Goke B, et al. 68Ga-DOTATATE PET/CT for the early prediction of response to somatostatin receptor-mediated radionuclide therapy in patients with well-differentiated neuroendocrine tumors. *Journal of nuclear medicine:* official publication, Society of Nuclear Medicine. 2010;51(9):1349-56. Epub 2010/08/20.

[114] Nicolas G, Giovacchini G, Muller-Brand J, Forrer F. Targeted radiotherapy with radiolabeled somatostatin analogs. *Endocrinology and metabolism clinics of North America.* 2011;40(1):187-204, ix-x. Epub 2011/02/26.

[115] Oberg K. Molecular Imaging Radiotherapy: Theranostics for Personalized Patient Management of Neuroendocrine Tumors (NETs). *Theranostics.* 2012;2(5):448-58. Epub 2012/07/07.

[116] Wehrmann C, Senftleben S, Zachert C, Muller D, Baum RP. Results of individual patient dosimetry in peptide receptor radionuclide therapy with 177Lu DOTA-TATE and 177Lu DOTA-NOC. *Cancer biotherapy and radiopharmaceuticals.* 2007;22(3):406-16. Epub 2007/07/27.

[117] Roesch F, Riss PJ. The renaissance of the (6)(8)Ge/(6)(8)Ga radionuclide generator initiates new developments in (6)(8)Ga radiopharmaceutical chemistry. *Current topics in medicinal chemistry.* 2010;10(16):1633-68. Epub 2010/06/30.

[118] Breeman WA, Verbruggen AM. The 68Ge/ 68Ga generator has high potential, but when can we use 68Ga-labelled tracers in clinical routine? *European Journal of Nuclear Medicine and Molecular Imaging.* 2007; 34(7):978-81. Epub 2007/03/03.

[119] Zhernosekov KP, Filosofov DV, Baum RP, Aschoff P, Bihl H, Razbash AA, et al. Processing of generator-produced 68Ga for medical application. *Journal of Nuclear Medicine* : official publication, Society of Nuclear Medicine. 2007;48(10):1741-8. Epub 2007/09/18.

[120] Weiner RE, Thakur ML. Chemistry of Gallium and Indium Radiopharmaceuticals. In: Welch MJ, Redvanly CS, editors. *Handbook of Radiopharmaceuticals Radiochemistry and Applications.* Chichester, West Sussex, England: John Wiley and Sons Ltd.; 2003. p. 363-99.

[121] Draft monograph proposal. Gallium (68Ga) chloride solution for radiolabelling.: *European Pharmacopoeia*; 2011a; Available from: http://www.eanm.org/committees/radiopharmacy/Gallium_233E.pdf?PH PSESSID=06a4ca4cfb4fc26b12455abcfb77dd69.

[122] Blom E, Koziorowski J. 68Ga-autoclabeling of DOTA-TATE and DOTA-NOC. *Applied radiation and isotopes : including data, instrumentation and methods for use in agriculture, industry and medicine.* 2012;70(6):980-3. Epub 2012/04/07.

[123] Moi MK, Meares CF, Denardo SJ. The peptide way to macrocyclic bifunctional chelating agents: synthesis of 2-(p-nitrobenzyl)-1,4,7,10-tetraazacyclododecane-N,N',N'',N'''-tetraacetic acid and study of its yttrium(III) complex. *Journal of the American Chemical Society.* 1988; 110(18):6266-7. Epub 1988/08/01.

[124] Bartholoma MD. Recent developments in the design of bifunctional chelators for metal-based radiopharmaceuticals used in Positron Emission Tomography. *Inorg. Chem. Acta.* 2012;389:36-51.

[125] Virgolini I, Ambrosini V, Bomanji JB, Baum RP, Fanti S, Gabriel M, et al. Procedure guidelines for PET/CT tumour imaging with 68Ga-DOTA-conjugated peptides: 68Ga-DOTA-TOC, 68Ga-DOTA-NOC, 68Ga-

DOTA-TATE. *European Journal of Nuclear Medicine and Molecular Imaging*. 2010;37(10):2004-10. Epub 2010/07/03.

[126] Castellucci P, Pou Ucha J, Fuccio C, Rubello D, Ambrosini V, Montini GC, et al. Incidence of increased 68Ga-DOTANOC uptake in the pancreatic head in a large series of extrapancreatic NET patients studied with sequential PET/CT. *Journal of Nuclear Medicine:* official publication, Society of Nuclear Medicine. 2011;52(6):886-90. Epub 2011/05/17.

[127] Velikyan I, Sundin A, Eriksson B, Lundqvist H, Sorensen J, Bergstrom M, et al. In vivo binding of [68Ga]-DOTATOC to somatostatin receptors in neuroendocrine tumours--impact of peptide mass. *Nuclear medicine and biology*. 2010;37(3):265-75. Epub 2010/03/30.

[128] de Jong M, Breeman WA, Bernard BF, van Gameren A, de Bruin E, Bakker WH, et al. Tumour uptake of the radiolabelled somatostatin analogue [DOTA0, TYR3]octreotide is dependent on the peptide amount. *European Journal of Nuclear Medicine*. 1999;26(7):693-8. Epub 1999/07/10.

[129] Bernhardt P, Kolby L, Johanson V, Nilsson O, Ahlman H, Forssell-Aronsson E. Biodistribution of 111in-DTPA-D-Phe1-octreotide in tumor-bearing nude mice: influence of amount injected and route of administration. *Nuclear medicine and biology*. 2003;30(3):253-60. Epub 2003/05/15.

[130] Schuhmacher J, Zhang H, Doll J, Macke HR, Matys R, Hauser H, et al. GRP receptor-targeted PET of a rat pancreas carcinoma xenograft in nude mice with a 68Ga-labeled bombesin(6-14) analog. *Journal of nuclear medicine:* official publication, Society of Nuclear Medicine. 2005;46(4):691-9. Epub 2005/04/06.

[131] Tolmachev V, Rosik D, Wallberg H, Sjoberg A, Sandstrom M, Hansson M, et al. Imaging of EGFR expression in murine xenografts using site-specifically labelled anti-EGFR 111In-DOTA-Z EGFR:2377 Affibody molecule: aspect of the injected tracer amount. *European Journal of Nuclear Medicine and Molecular Imaging*. 2010;37(3):613-22. Epub 2009/10/20.

[132] Tolmachev V, Wallberg H, Sandstrom M, Hansson M, Wennborg A, Orlova A. Optimal specific radioactivity of anti-HER2 Affibody molecules enables discrimination between xenografts with high and low HER2 expression levels. *European Journal of Nuclear Medicine and Molecular Imaging*. 2011;38(3):531-9. Epub 2010/11/12.

[133] Pandit-Taskar N, O'Donoghue JA, Morris MJ, Wills EA, Schwartz LH, Gonen M, et al. Antibody mass escalation study in patients with castration-resistant prostate cancer using 111In-J591: lesion detectability and dosimetric projections for 90Y radioimmunotherapy. *Journal of Nuclear Medicine:* official publication, Society of Nuclear Medicine. 2008;49(7):1066-74. Epub 2008/06/17.

[134] Schreiter NF, Brenner W, Nogami M, Buchert R, Huppertz A, Pape UF, et al. Cost comparison of 111In-DTPA-octreotide scintigraphy and 68Ga-DOTATOC PET/CT for staging enteropancreatic neuroendocrine tumours. *European Journal of Nuclear Medicine and Molecular Imaging.* 2012;39(1):72-82. Epub 2011/09/20.

[135] Otte A, Jermann E, Behe M, Goetze M, Bucher HC, Roser HW, et al. DOTATOC: a powerful new tool for receptor-mediated radionuclide therapy. *European Journal of Nuclear Medicine.* 1997;24(7):792-5. Epub 1997/07/01.

[136] de Jong M, Bakker WH, Krenning EP, Breeman WA, van der Pluijm ME, Bernard BF, et al. Yttrium-90 and indium-111 labelling, receptor binding and biodistribution of [DOTA0,d-Phe1,Tyr3]octreotide, a promising somatostatin analogue for radionuclide therapy. *European Journal of Nuclear Medicine.* 1997;24(4):368-71. Epub 1997/04/01.

[137] Bernard BF, Krenning EP, Breeman WA, Rolleman EJ, Bakker WH, Visser TJ, et al. D-lysine reduction of indium-111 octreotide and yttrium-90 octreotide renal uptake. *Journal of Nuclear Medicine :* official publication, Society of Nuclear Medicine. 1997;38(12):1929-33. Epub 1998/01/16.

[138] Henze M, Schuhmacher J, Hipp P, Kowalski J, Becker DW, Doll J, et al. PET imaging of somatostatin receptors using [68GA]DOTA-D-Phe1-Tyr3-octreotide: first results in patients with meningiomas. *Journal of Nuclear Medicine:* official publication, Society of Nuclear Medicine. 2001;42(7):1053-6. Epub 2001/07/05.

[139] Gehler B, Paulsen F, Oksuz MO, Hauser TK, Eschmann SM, Bares R, et al. [68Ga]-DOTATOC-PET/CT for meningioma IMRT treatment planning. *Radiat. Oncol.* 2009;4:56. Epub 2009/11/20.

[140] Ruf J, Heuck F, Schiefer J, Denecke T, Elgeti F, Pascher A, et al. Impact of Multiphase 68Ga-DOTATOC-PET/CT on therapy management in patients with neuroendocrine tumors. *Neuroendocrinology.* 2010; 91(1): 101-9. Epub 2009/12/10.

[141] Frilling A, Sotiropoulos GC, Radtke A, Malago M, Bockisch A, Kuehl H, et al. The impact of 68Ga-DOTATOC positron emission

tomography/computed tomography on the multimodal management of patients with neuroendocrine tumors. *Annals of surgery.* 2010;252(5): 850-6. Epub 2010/11/03.

[142] Thorwarth D, Henke G, Muller AC, Reimold M, Beyer T, Boss A, et al. Simultaneous 68Ga-DOTATOC-PET/MRI for IMRT treatment planning for meningioma: first experience. *International Journal of Radiation Oncology, Biology, Physics.* 2011;81(1):277-83. Epub 2011/02/09.

[143] Schreiter NF, Nogami M, Steffen I, Pape UF, Hamm B, Brenner W, et al. Evaluation of the potential of PET-MRI fusion for detection of liver metastases in patients with neuroendocrine tumours. *European radiology.* 2012;22(2):458-67. Epub 2011/09/10.

[144] Lewis JS, Laforest R, Lewis MR, Anderson CJ. Comparative dosimetry of copper-64 and yttrium-90-labeled somatostatin analogs in a tumor-bearing rat model. *Cancer biotherapy and radiopharmaceuticals.* 2000; 15(6):593-604. Epub 2001/02/24.

[145] Win Z, Rahman L, Murrell J, Todd J, Al-Nahhas A. The possible role of 68Ga-DOTATATE PET in malignant abdominal paraganglioma. *European Journal of Nuclear Medicine and Molecular Imaging.* 2006; 33(4):506. Epub 2006/02/02.

[146] Lewington VJ. Targeted radionuclide therapy for neuroendocrine tumours. *Endocrine-related cancer.* 2003;10(4):497-501. Epub 2004/01/10.

[147] Win Z, Al-Nahhas A, Rubello D, Gross MD. Somatostatin receptor PET imaging with Gallium-68 labeled peptides. *Q. J. Nucl. Med. Mol. Imaging.* 2007;51(3):244-50. Epub 2007/04/28.

[148] Naji M, Zhao C, Welsh SJ, Meades R, Win Z, Ferrarese A, et al. 68Ga-DOTA-TATE PET vs. 123I-MIBG in identifying malignant neural crest tumours. *Molecular imaging and biology : MIB : the official publication of the Academy of Molecular Imaging.* 2011;13(4):769-75. Epub 2010/08/12.

[149] Hofman MS, Kong G, Neels OC, Eu P, Hong E, Hicks RJ. High management impact of Ga-68 DOTATATE (GaTate) PET/CT for imaging neuroendocrine and other somatostatin expressing tumours. *Journal of Medical Imaging and Radiation Oncology.* 2012;56(1):40-7. Epub 2012/02/22.

[150] Rominger A, Saam T, Vogl E, Ubleis C, la Fougere C, Forster S, et al. In vivo imaging of macrophage activity in the coronary arteries using 68Ga-DOTATATE PET/CT: correlation with coronary calcium burden

and risk factors. *Journal of Nuclear Medicine*: official publication, Society of Nuclear Medicine. 2010;51(2):193-7. Epub 2010/01/19.

[151] Kabasakal L, Demirci E, Ocak M, Decristoforo C, Araman A, Ozsoy Y, et al. Comparison of (68)Ga-DOTATATE and (68)Ga-DOTANOC PET/CT imaging in the same patient group with neuroendocrine tumours. *European Journal of Nuclear Medicine and Molecular Imaging*. 2012;39(8):1271-7. Epub 2012/04/25.

[152] Poeppel TD, Binse I, Petersenn S, Lahner H, Schott M, Antoch G, et al. 68Ga-DOTATOC versus 68Ga-DOTATATE PET/CT in functional imaging of neuroendocrine tumors. *Journal of Nuclear Medicine*: official publication, Society of Nuclear Medicine. 2011;52(12):1864-70. Epub 2011/11/11.

[153] Lapinska G, Bryszewska M, Fijolek-Warszewska A, Kozlowicz-Gudzinska I, Ochman P, Sackiewicz-Slaby A. The diagnostic role of 68Ga-DOTATATE PET/CT in the detection of neuroendocrine tumours. *Nuclear medicine review Central and Eastern Europe*. 2011;14(1):16-20. Epub 2011/07/14.

[154] Wild D, Macke HR, Waser B, Reubi JC, Ginj M, Rasch H, et al. 68Ga-DOTANOC: a first compound for PET imaging with high affinity for somatostatin receptor subtypes 2 and 5. *European Journal of Nuclear Medicine and Molecular Imaging*. 2005;32(6):724. Epub 2004/11/20.

[155] Naswa N, Sharma P, Kumar A, Soundararajan R, Kumar R, Malhotra A, et al. (6)(8)Ga-DOTANOC PET/CT in patients with carcinoma of unknown primary of neuroendocrine origin. *Clinical nuclear medicine*. 2012;37(3):245-51. Epub 2012/02/09.

[156] Prasad V, Ambrosini V, Hommann M, Hoersch D, Fanti S, Baum RP. Detection of unknown primary neuroendocrine tumours (CUP-NET) using (68)Ga-DOTA-NOC receptor PET/CT. *European Journal of Nuclear Medicine and Molecular Imaging*. 2010;37(1):67-77. Epub 2009/07/21.

[157] Campana D, Ambrosini V, Pezzilli R, Fanti S, Labate AM, Santini D, et al. Standardized uptake values of (68)Ga-DOTANOC PET: a promising prognostic tool in neuroendocrine tumors. *Journal of Nuclear Medicine*: official publication, Society of Nuclear Medicine. 2010;51(3):353-9. Epub 2010/02/13.

[158] Pettinato C, Sarnelli A, Di Donna M, Civollani S, Nanni C, Montini G, et al. 68Ga-DOTANOC: biodistribution and dosimetry in patients affected by neuroendocrine tumors. *European Journal of Nuclear Medicine and Molecular Imaging*. 2008;35(1):72-9. Epub 2007/09/18.

[159] Ambrosini V, Campana D, Bodei L, Nanni C, Castellucci P, Allegri V, et al. 68Ga-DOTANOC PET/CT clinical impact in patients with neuroendocrine tumors. *Journal of Nuclear Medicine*: official publication, Society of Nuclear Medicine. 2010;51(5):669-73. Epub 2010/04/17.

[160] Nicolini S, Valentina A, Lorenzo F, Stefano F. 68Ga DOTANOC PET/CT detects medullary thyroid cancer relapse at bone level. *Clinical nuclear medicine*. 2012;37(6):591-2. Epub 2012/05/23.

[161] Ambrosini V, Zompatori M, De Luca F, Antonia D, Allegri V, Nanni C, et al. 68Ga-DOTANOC PET/CT allows somatostatin receptor imaging in idiopathic pulmonary fibrosis: preliminary results. *Journal of Nuclear Medicine*: official publication, Society of Nuclear Medicine. 2010; 51(12): 1950-5. Epub 2010/11/17.

[162] Naswa N, Kumar A, Sharma P, Bal C, Malhotra A, Kumar R. Imaging carotid body chemodectomas with 68Ga-DOTA-NOC PET-CT. *The British Journal of Radiology*. 2012; 85(1016): 1140-5. Epub 2011/11/19.

[163] Li WP, Meyer LA, Anderson CJ. Radiopharmaceuticals for positron emission tomography imaging of somatostatin receptor positive tumors. *Top Curr. Chem.* 2005;252:179-92.

[164] Sun X, Wuest M, Weisman GR, Wong EH, Reed DP, Boswell CA, et al. Radiolabeling and in vivo behavior of copper-64-labeled cross-bridged cyclam ligands. *Journal of Medicinal Chemistry*. 2002;45(2):469-77. Epub 2002/01/11.

[165] Boswell CA, Sun X, Niu W, Weisman GR, Wong EH, Rheingold AL, et al. Comparative in vivo stability of copper-64-labeled cross-bridged and conventional tetraazamacrocyclic complexes. *Journal of Medicinal Chemistry*. 2004;47(6):1465-74. Epub 2004/03/05.

[166] Wester HJ, Schottelius M, Poethko T, Bruus-Jensen K, Schwaiger M. Radiolabeled carbohydrated somatostatin analogs: a review of the current status. *Cancer biotherapy and radiopharmaceuticals*. 2004; 19(2): 231-44. Epub 2004/06/10.

[167] Schottelius M, Poethko T, Herz M, Reubi JC, Kessler H, Schwaiger M, et al. First (18)F-labeled tracer suitable for routine clinical imaging of sst receptor-expressing tumors using positron emission tomography. *Clinical Cancer Research: An Official Journal of the American Association for Cancer Research*. 2004;10(11):3593-606. Epub 2004/06/03.

[168] Laverman P, D'Souza CA, Eek A, McBride WJ, Sharkey RM, Oyen WJ, et al. Optimized labeling of NOTA-conjugated octreotide with F-18. *Tumour biology: The Journal of the International Society for Oncodevelopmental Biology and Medicine.* 2012;33(2):427-34. Epub 2011/10/20.

[169] Laverman P, McBride WJ, Sharkey RM, Eek A, Joosten L, Oyen WJ, et al. A novel facile method of labeling octreotide with (18)F-fluorine. *Journal of Nuclear Medicine:* official publication, Society of Nuclear Medicine. 2010;51(3):454-61. Epub 2010/02/13.

In: Somatostatin   ISBN: 978-1-62417-419-3
Editors: A. Anderson and T. McAnulty © 2013 Nova Science Publishers, Inc.

Chapter 3

SOMATOSTATIN ANALOGS AS A TREATMENT FOR CONGENITAL HYPERINSULINISM

Kineret Mazor-Aronovitch and Dalit Modan-Moses[*]

Pediatric Endocrinology and Diabetes Unit, The Edmond and Lily Safra
Children's Hospital, Chaim Sheba Medical Center, Tel-Hashomer, Israel

ABSTRACT

Congenital hyperinsulinism (CHI) is a functional disorder of insulin
secretion. The long-term outcome of infants with CHI depends on the
prevention of hypoglycemic episodes to avoid the high risk of permanent
brain damage including psychomotor retardation, seizures, and learning
disabilities. In its diffuse severe form, it is traditionally treated with near-
total pancreatectomy. However, even after this procedure normoglycemia
is not always achieved, and many patients develop diabetes mellitus at
puberty.

Human β-cells show a high expression of somatostatin receptors,
particularly type 2 (SSTR2), and somatostatin directly suppresses insulin
release. It was therefore hypothesized that somatostatin could be used as a
therapeutic agent in CHI. This hypothesis was successfully tested as early

---

[*] Correspondence to :Dalit Modan-Moses, M.D ,.Pediatric Endocrinology and Diabetes Unit ,
The Edmond and Lily Safra Children's Hospital ,Chaim Sheba Medical Center ,Tel-
Hashomer, 52621 Israel, Tel: +972-3-5305015 Fax: +972-3-5305055, e-mail:
dmodan@sheba.health.gov.il.

as 1977, but clinical implementation was limited by the short half-life of native somatostatin. With the advent of the first somatostatin analog, octreotide, in the 1980's, a conservative approach to the treatment of CHI was developed, using octreotide administered subcutaneously by injection or through a pump, in combination with other medications (diazoxide, glucagon), as well as frequent or continuous feeding by means of a gastrostomy tube. Using this approach it is possible to achieve euglycemia, normal growth and good neurodevelopmental outcome, at least in some patients' groups. Potential side effects of treatment with somatostatin include cholelithiasis, impaired growth, and impaired thyroid function. However, the only side effect we usually encounter is asymptomatic cholelithiasis. Despite our success with the conservative approach, the treatment may pose a huge burden and be stressful for the patients and families. Recently, we and others reported successful treatment with the long –acting somatostatin analogs lanreotide acetate and octretide LAR, administered once-monthly, and resulting in simplification of daily care and improved quality of life.

INTRODUCTION

The peptide hormone somatostatin , discovered by Brazeau et al. [1], is a cyclopeptide consisting of 14 or 28 amino acids which is expressed in many tissues throughout the body including the central nervous system, hypothalamus, gastrointestinal tract, and the pancreas. Somatostatin peptides bind with high affinity to somatostatin receptors expressed on target tissues, thereby exerting a large number of biological effects. Somatostatins are important regulators of endocrine and exocrine secretion and affect the release of many hormones such as growth hormone (GH), glucagon, insulin, gastrin, secretin and thyroid stimulating hormone (TSH). In the central nervous system somatostatin peptides act as neuromodulators and neurotransmitters [2].

The biological effects of somatostatin are mediated by G-protein-coupled somatostatin receptors, of which five human receptor subtypes, hsst1-5, have been cloned [3]. The sequence homology between receptor subtypes varies between 39 and 57% with great sequence homology seen in the transmembrane domains [4]. All five somatostatin receptor subtypes modulate various intracellular signaling pathways such as adenylyl cyclase, ion channels (K+, Ca2+), serine/threonine-and tyrosine-phosphatases as well as phospholipase A2 [5].

CONGENITAL HYPERINSULINISM OF INFANCY (CHI)

The term congenital hyperinsulinism of infancy (CHI) describes a group of genetic disorders characterized by inadequate suppression of insulin secretion in the presence of recurrent hypoglycemia. It is the most common cause of persistent hypoglycemia in infancy [6]. Mutations in 8 genes have been associated with CHI in the newborn period. The most frequent form of CHI is associated with recessive mutations of the potassium channel KATP. This channel is encoded by two adjacent genes on chromosome 11p15.1, SUR1 (ABCC8) and KIR 6.2 (KCNJ11). Two SUR1 (ABCC8) mutations, i.e. ΔF1388 and 3992-9g>a, appear to account for more than 90% of cases in the Ashkenazi Jewish population [7]. Two subtypes of CHI have been described: 1. A diffuse form of the disease manifested as diffuse beta cell hyperfunction in children with two mutant KATP alleles. 2. A focal form manifested as small discrete areas of beta cell adenomatosis, surrounded by normally functioning islets. These children have a paternally derived KATP mutation and loss of maternal 11p15 allele restricted to the pancreatic lesion [8].

Other gene defects associated with CHI include activating mutations of glutamate dehydrogenase (GDH) and glucokinase (GK), short-chain 3-hydroxyacyl-CoA dehydrogenase (short-chain 3-hydroxyacyl-CoA dehydro-genase (SCHAD), ectopic expression on β-cell plasma membrane of monocarboxylate transporter 1 (MCT1; encoded by SLC16A1), hepatocyte nuclear factor 4α (HNF-4α), and uncoupling protein 2 (UCP2) [9].

Despite the new knowledge of pathogenesis and genetics of the disease, the management still presents pediatricians with a choice of unsatisfactory treatments that have major long term implications for the child and the family. Surgery (partial pancreatectomy for focal disease and near-total pancreatectomy for diffuse disease) is still considered the treatment of choice by some groups [9]. However, it became evident that near-total pancreatectomy in patients with diffuse disease often failed to cure the hypoglycemia and led to diabetes mellitus [10]: while more than 90% of focal CHI cases were proven to be cured after surgery, in cases of diffuse CHI, approximately 50% of cases continued to have hypoglycemia in the days after surgery [9, 10] and 25% showed signs of insulin-insufficiency requiring insulin treatment [9]. By 13 years of age, the incidence of hyperglycemia in one large series reached 100% [10].

These findings, as well as the observation that most patients with milder disease entered clinical remission with no need for medication, generated the pursuit of medical management of CHI.

The introduction of diazoxide, a KATP channel agonist, in 1965 allowed 20-30% of patients to be managed without surgery. The main side effects of this treatment are fluid retention which may lead to edema or congestive heart failure, and hypertrichosis [11].

THE RATIONAL FOR USING SOMATOSTATIN AND ITS ANALOGS IN CHI

Human pancreatic islet cells express all five somatostatin subtypes, as determined by immunohistochemistry [12, 13]. In beta-cells, sst1, sst2, and sst5 receptors are the most abundantly expressed subtypes [13]. Somatostatin inhibits insulin release through different mechanisms involving adenylyl cyclase and protein kinase A [14], decreasing cAMP accumulation and stimulating the activity of KATP channels in pancreatic beta cells [15]. In addition, it inhibits insulin gene expression [16, 17]. In rodents, the inhibition of insulin secretion seems to be primarily mediated by sst5 [18]. In humans, limited, conflicting data have been obtained, with roles suggested for both sst2 [19] and sst5 [13, 20].

INITIAL "PROOF OF CONCEPT" STUDIES

The use of somatostatin for treatment of hyperinsulinism in infancy was first reported in 1977 by Hirsch et al. [21]. The authors treated a 2 month old infant with severe intractable hypoglycemia. A dose-dependent rise in blood glucose and concomitant suppression of serum insulin levels was observed, with minimal suppression of plasma glucagon levels. Single subcutaneous injections of 50 µg protamine zinc somatostatin raised preprandial blood glucose levels to 83±3 mg/dl for 4-5 days.

Similar experience was reported in 1983 with 2 infants who were admitted for severe, intractable hypoglycemia [22]. Somatostatin was infused to test the individual sensitivity of the β-cells. Basal and glucose-induced insulin and C-peptide secretion were significantly reduced. Preoperative treatment with somatostatin was introduced, which controlled the hypoglycemia.

SOMATOSTATIN ANALOGS AS A TREATMENT OF CHI

Natural somatostatin undergoes rapid proteolytic degradation in plasma and has a short half life ($t_{1/2}$ <3min). Hence, it is effective only when given by continuous infusion, precluding its use as part of an effective home regimen.

Octreotide, an analog of somatostatin, has a longer duration of action and is more potent than the native peptide. It has been used extensively in the treatment of patients with carcinoid syndrome, vasoactive intestinal peptide-related neoplasms, glucagonomas and acromegaly. It was first used in the treatment of CHI in 1986, in a neonate with severe hypoglycemia and convulsive episodes [23]. Intravenous infusion of octreotide at a dosage gradually increasing from 2 to 50 microgm/day was accompanied by a dramatic fall in circulating insulin levels. Glucose homeostasis was restored and convulsive spells ceased. Fasting blood glucose levels stabilized between 60-85mg/dl (3.4 and 4.7 mmol/l). No rebound phenomenon was observed during short term interruptions of octreotide infusion. Subtotal pancreatectomy was performed during treatment

The majority of reports in the following years have described octreotide use in single patients. The first reports were of short term treatment allowing the stabilization of CHI patients before pancreatectomy, lowering glucose requirements and avoiding fluid retention induced by diazoxide treatment.

The first report of long term use of octreotide was published in 1987 [24], describing an infant who had a subtotal pancreatectomy at the age of 4 weeks, but at the age of 8 months had recurrent hypoglycemia. The infant responded well to 4 daily injections of octreotide, and was discharged with a computerized infusion pump injecting octreotide every 3 hours and thereafter every 4 hours. At the time of writing, the child has been treated for 21 months. Her gains in height and weight were described as satisfactory [24].

In 1989 Glaser et al. reported the first case of CHI patient treated with octreotide alone as an outpatient for 17 months, without requiring surgery [25]. The decision to attempt medical treatment was based on the observation of patients with CHI who entered remission in infancy after being scheduled for surgery that had been delayed for various unrelated reasons.

The first two large series of CHI patients with long term treatment with octreotide were reported simultaneously in 1993 by Glaser, Hirsch and Landau [26] and by Thornton et al. [27].

Thornton et al. described their experience with octreotide treatment in 16 CHI patients who did not respond to diazoxide. The patients were treated with 3-6 s.c. injections a day. In 7 patients with onset of severe hypoglycemia in the first days of life, octreotide was helpful in stabilizing plasma glucose levels and allowed reductions in the rates of glucose infusion. However, glucose control was inadequate to avoid subtotal pancreatectomy. In 7 other patients, a trial of long term treatment with octreotide was undertaken. Four were treated successfully for up to 4.3 years, avoiding surgery. Two patients with early onset hypoglycemia who were stabilized with octreotide before pancreatectomy, also needed it after surgery because of persistent hypoglycemia. Octreotide therapy was not associated with thyroid deficiency and caused only transient malabsorption. All patients receiving long term therapy had some decrease in linear growth and 2 had subnormal plasma concentration of IGF-1 and IGFBP-3, suggesting growth hormone suppression by octreotide. Resistance to octreotide therapy, even with increasing doses (tachyphylaxis), occurred in all patients [27].

Glaser et al. described their experience in 15 CHI patients treated with octreotide. Seven patients subsequently underwent partial pancreatectomy. Four of these patients responded well to octreotide, but their family situation did not permit long term parenteral treatment. CHI was controlled with octreotide alone in the remaining 8 patients. Octreotide, 3-10micg/kg/day, was given as 3-4 daily s.c. injections in 4 patients and as continuous s.c. infusion using an insulin infusion pump in the other four. Frequent feedings and raw cornstarch at night were required by all patients, along with octreotide. All had mild, transient gastrointestinal symptoms (vomiting, abdominal distention, steatorrhea) after the start of therapy. Asymptomatic gallstones were found in 1 patient after 1 year of treatment. No other long term untoward effects were noted, including no detrimental effects on psychomotor development. There was a transient growth deceleration in all patients during the initial months of treatment, followed by normalization of the growth rate. Growth was not affected in 5 of 6 patients treated for more than 6 months.

In 5 patients octreotide was discontinued after 8 months to 5.5 years; one patient required no further treatment, 2 patients were given diazoxide, and 2 required percutaneous gastrostomy. At the time of publication, 3 patients (aged 5-9 months) were still treated with octreotide. The authors concluded that aggressive medical treatment with octreotide together with frequent feedings, the addition of raw cornstarch at bedtime, and possibly diazoxide, is preferable to pancreatectomy [26].

It is noteworthy that conservative treatment was initiated before the genetics of CHI were elucidated, thus the pathology of diffuse or focal disease was not known in these patients.

Over the following years more experience with somatostatin analogs was gained. Data from the German registry for CHI reported a gradual switch from surgery to conservative treatment, especially in diffuse disease: before 1990 most patients (75%) were treated by subtotal pancreatectomy, whereas after 2000 only 4/68 patients were operated [28].

In 2007 we published our long term results of conservative treatment [29]. The study included 21 Ashkenazi CHI medically treated patients: 11 homozygotes (diffuse disease) and 9 heterozygotes with mutations on the paternal allele (presumed focal disease). In 18/21 of patients molecular genetic diagnosis was done in retrospect. The mean age at the time of the study was 13.7 years (range 8–23). There was no difference in the treatment and in the neurodevelopmental outcome between diffuse and presumed focal forms of the disease. Clinical remission occurred in all patients and this happened significantly earlier in patients with presumed focal disease (median = 1.7 years) than diffuse disease (5 years). In 4 patients with diffuse disease, occasional isolated documented hypoglycemic episodes occurred at home, years after all medications were withdrawn. These episodes occurred during acute gastroenteritis in one patient and after introducing a strict regime of diet and exercise for obesity in another. In the remaining 2 patients, no clear cause for the hypoglycemia was evident.

Patients' heights in both groups were appropriate for parental target height, except for one short patient. Three patients were obese and 4 patients were overweight. In 3 of these patients, there was a family history of obesity. Regarding the neurodevelopmental outcome, 10 CHI patients had perinatal seizures of short duration. Four had post-neonatal seizures, which remitted entirely. During early childhood, 4 patients (19%) had hypotonia, 8 patients (38%) had fine motor problems, 7 patients (33%) had gross motor problems (clumsiness), and one had mild cerebral palsy. Three patients (14%) had speech problems. Eight patients required developmental therapy, compared to one in the control group. Most of these problems were resolved by the age of 4–5 years. At school age, all were enrolled in regular education, some excelled in their studies, 6 out of 21 patients (29%) had learning problems (comparing to 2/21 controls).

There is still controversy regarding the optimal treatment for CHI. While we as well as other groups [28] have been able to manage most of our patients over the last 25 years using the conservative approach, other groups report a much lower rate of success (10-15%) with this approach, and advocate pancreatectomy [9]. There are several possible reasons for this discrepancy. First, our definition of response to medical therapy is different. Palladino et al.

define medical response as the ability to maintain glucose above 70 mg/dl during a fast of >10-12 hours [9]. However, we believe that in young infants this definition is too strict. The generally adopted plasma glucose concentration that defines neonatal hypoglycemia is <47 mg/dL [30]. Hence, in our opinion, a threshold of 60mg/dl is acceptable in infants with CHI treated medically.

Moreover, an aggressive nutritional approach is a mainstay of our protocol. We instruct parents to feed infants every 3-4 hours (similar to the feeding pattern of normal neonates), adding continuous night feedings via gastrostomy if needed, and do not expect them to tolerate more than 5-6 hours of fasting.

Many of our patients are Ashkenasi Jews who have one of 2 known mutations, so it could be argued that our group is homogenous and is not comparable to patient populations in other countries. However, we have seen the same results for conservative treatment in patients with other mutations and in patients with no known mutations.

Finally, in patients with typical Ashkenasi mutations in Israel, the genetic diagnosis of CHI is often made very quickly, within a few days of presentation. This allows us to institute treatment very early, and may contribute to our favorable long-term results.

THE RATIONAL FOR USING LONG-ACTING SOMATOSTATIN ANALOGS

Despite the success with the conservative approach, the treatment may pose a huge burden and be stressful for the patients and families. Octeotide has a half-life of 90 minutes, and is therefore administered subcutaneously either by multiple subcutaneous injections (every 6–8 h) or by continuous infusion via a pump, demanding intensive daily care.

Around the age of 2 years, some of the parents encounter technical problems with the pump, as the children are prone to play with the pump and pull out the catheters. It is also very difficult to place the children in day care, because they need continuous supervision. Treatment with a long-acting somatostatin analog may simplify the daily care of patients and improve their quality of life.

LONG ACTING SOMATOSTATIN ANALOGS

Long acting somatostatin analogs were developed in order to increase dosing interval and provide a more sustained clinical effect. The analogs lack the key enzyme cleavage sites, and are therefore more stable than native somatostatin. Hence, the synthetic analogs have similar activity to native somatostatin, but with a longer half-life.

Three long acting somatostatin analogs are currently available: lanreotide SR, octreotide LAR, and pasireotide (SOM 230). Lanreotide SR and octreotide LAR are comprised of eight amino acids with a disulphide bridge, and are formulated as microspheres of biodegradable polymer containing the active peptide [31].

Both agents bind preferentially with high affinity to the sst2 subtype, have reduced affinity for sst3 and sst5, and show very low or absent binding affinity for type 1 and type 4 receptors [32, 33].

In contrast, Pasireotide is a metabolically stable cyclohexapeptide, binding with high affinity to sst1, sst2, sst3 and sst5 and with lower affinity to sst4 [2, 33, 34].

Octreotide LAR (Sandostatin LAR) is injected intramuscularly every 4 weeks. Following a single IM injection, serum octreotide concentration reaches a transient initial peak within 1 hour after administration, followed by a progressive decline to a low undetectable octreotide level within 24 hours. Levels remain low until 7 days after the initial injection; they then increase and plateau at about day 14, remaining relatively constant during the following 3 to 4 weeks. Octreotide concentrations reach steady-state after 3 intramuscular injections of octreotide LAR at 4-week intervals [35] .

Lanreotide acetate is available in a prolonged release (PR) formulation of encapsulated microspheres of biodegradable polymer [33, 36], which is injected every 7–28 days or as an aqueous slow-release depot preparation (Somatuline Autogel®), supplied in small-volume, prefilled syringes, which is administered every 28 days by deep subcutaneous injection [31, 33, 37].

After a single s.c. injection of the autogel, a maximum serum concentration is reached within 12 hours, followed by a slow decrease (apparent half-life: 33 ± 14 days).

Steady state serum levels of lanreotide are reached, on average, after 4 injections every 4 weeks [31, 38].

LONG ACTING SOMATOSATIN ANALOGS IN PEDIATRIC PATIENTS

Long acting somatostatin analogs have been widely used as safe and effective treatments for pituitary and neuroendocrine tumors in adults [31, 33, 39], however experience with their use in pediatric patients is limited. Both octreotide LAR and lanreotide acetate have been used in a small number of adolescents for the treatment of thyroid eye disease [40], GH secreting adenomas [41], pituitary gigantism [42], thyrotropin-secreting pituitary adenoma [43] and hypothalamic obesity [44]. Recently, Carel et al. reported treating girls with constitutional tall stature with lanreotide PR 30 mg biweekly injections. Gastrointestinal adverse events and cholelithiasis were reported in 35/37 patients and 5/37 patients, respectively. There was one withdrawal due to gastrointestinal distress, but most patients continued long-term treatment [45].

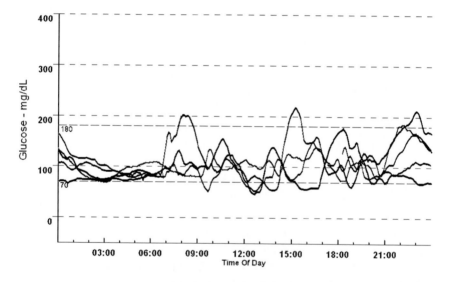

Figure 1. Ninety-six-hour glucose profile of patient 1 under treatment with a monthly injection of lanreotide acetate. CGMS was done during the fourth week after injection, at the time lanreotide levels would be expected to be the lowest .Reproduced with permission from Modan-Moses D et al. Treatment of congenital hyperinsulinism with lanreotide acetate (Somatuline Autogel). J Clin Endocrinol Metab. 2011 Aug;96(8):2312-7. Copyright 2011, The Endocrine Society.

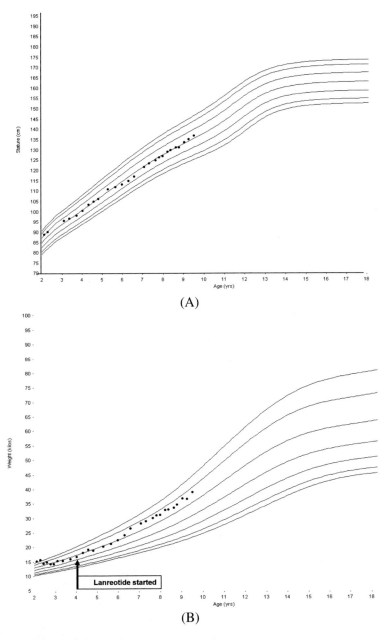

Figure 2. A, Growth curve of patient 1. B, Weight curve of patient 1. Reproduced with permission from Modan-Moses D et al. Treatment of congenital hyperinsulinism with lanreotide acetate (Somatuline Autogel). J Clin Endocrinol Metab. 2011 Aug;96(8):2312-7. Copyright 2011, The Endocrine Society.

Long Acting Somatosatin Analogs in CHI

Bakker and Oostdijk first described in 2006 the use of lanreotide in an 18 month old infant with CHI after failure of three pancreatectomies. The authors reported that continuous s.c. octreotide was successfully replaced by lanreotide 60 mg s.c. every 4 weeks by 18 months of age, but very little data was provided regarding length of treatment and clinical response [46].

We reported our favorable experience with the use of lanreotide acetate in two patients with CHI [47]. The first patient was of non-consanguineous Ashkenazi-Jewish descent, who was diagnosed shortly after birth and was found to be homozygous to the 3992 -9g>a ABCC8 (SUR1) mutation, while the second patient was of non-consanguineous Muslim Arab parents, diagnosed with hyperinsulinism at the age of 3 months, with no known Kir6.2/SUR1 mutations identified. Both patients were initially treated with diazoxide, hydrochlorothiazide, and frequent feeding with carbohydrate-enriched formula, with treatment with s.c. octreotide via pump added because of recurrent hypoglycemia. With this therapy, the patients were normoglycemic with a good growth rate, normal weight gain and excellent neurodevelopment. One of the patients had asymptomatic cholelithiasis detected by routine US at age 2 years. Both patients started around the age of 4 years lanreotide acetate, at a dose of 30 mg (55 microgm/kg/day), administered by deep subcutaneous injection once a month. Octreotide infusion was gradually weaned over a month. CGMS monitoring after discontinuation of pump therapy showed normoglycemia over 72 hours of monitoring. Our first patient has now been treated for nearly 7 years, and the second patient has been treated for 4 years. We were able to achieve good control of blood glucose levels, documented with CGMS (Figure 1), with no significant side effects. One patient showed a transient growth deceleration during the first two years of lanreotide acetate treatment, with subsequent catch-up growth and resumption of her previous height percentile (figure 2A). Neurodevelopment of both patients is excellent, weight gain was normal (figure 2B), and gall bladder US findings are stable. We recently were able to decrease the lanreotide dose to 20mg/month (18 microgm/kg/day) in one patient with maintenance of normoglyemia. The second patient required no increase in lanreotide dose to account for weight gain, and his current dose is 40microgm/kg/day. Patients and their families are very satisfied with the once-monthly injections and prefer it to pump therapy.

More recently, Le Quan Sang et al. described their experience with octreotide LAR in ten CHI patients (M=4, mean age at inclusion = 4.7 years), who have been well-controlled with s.c. octreotide [48]. The formal protocol lasted 6 months, and patients were followed up to 2 years after LAR initiation, with an average follow-up of 17 months. LAR was injected intramuscularly every 4 weeks, at a dose equal to the cumulative dose of s.c. octreotide over the 31 days prior to LAR initiation. Patients continued s.c. octreotide until the third injection of octreotide LAR, and at that time s.c. octreotide was stopped. Pain induced by IM injection was prevented by the use of xylocaine cream at the injection point and the intra-rectal administration of nalbuphine and midazolam. For the first 6 injections, patients were hospitalized every 4 weeks for 48–72h, during which blood glucose levels were closely monitored. For all ten patients, glycemias were maintained in the usual range, with rare and isolated events of hypoglycemia. HbA1c and IGF1 were unchanged compared to values under s.c. octreotide. The mean weight and height of the patients showed a normal increase, and no gallbladder stones were detected in the abdominal US performed during the study period. No side effect was noted during the study and the later follow-up. Plasma octreotide levels were stable under LAR octreotide. A parents' satisfaction questionnaire assessed at the end of the trial qualified LAR treatment as 'excellent' in 100% of parents, because it significantly improved their quality of life (QoL). Interestingly, QoL evaluations of the children were not able to detect any change after the treatment was switched.

CONCLUSION

Treatment of congenital hyperinsulinism with somatostatin analogs as a conservative management option was introduced in 1986. To date, our group has treated about 40 patients, achieving euglycemia, normal growth and normal neurodevelopment: school-aged children were all enrolled in regular education, and some excelled in their studies. Side effects of octreotide were minimal and included transient vomiting, diarrhea, abdominal distention and steatorrhea during the first weeks of treatment, biliary sludge, asymptomatic cholelithiasis and transient growth deceleration. Clinical remission occurred in all patients and they could be weaned off somatostatin analog therapy at a mean age of 5 years (range 1.5-12 y). Glucose intolerance has been described in some of these patients, however only one of them developed overt diabetes mellitus during follow-up of up to 23 years, and this patient is managed with diet alone. In contrast, all of our patients who underwent pancreatectomy subsequently developed diabetes mellitus. Similar results were reported by other groups: in a recent large follow up study including 58 patients with diffuse CHI who underwent pancreatectomy, hyperglycemia was found in 53% of the patients immediately after surgery; and in all patients at 13 years [10].

Long acting somatostatin analogs may present a safe and effective alternative to octreotide pump therapy in patients with CHI, offering an improved quality of life. The decision at what age to switch from s.c. octreotide therapy to lanreotide autogel should be individualized based on the size of the child and the difficulties the family has with pump or injection therapy. Our present policy is to offer lanreotide acetate to patients who are well-controlled on s.c. octreotide when they begin attending day care, as at this time the families often encounter difficulties with pump therapy.

Several issues still need to be elucidated. Longer follow-up of a larger patient group is needed to establish this new therapeutic option for CHI patients and to define the optimal age for initiating treatment, optimal dose, and differences between the different long-acting somatostatin analogs available. Octretide LAR and lanreotide autogel seem to be equally effective in controlling blood glucose levels, and similarly had minimal side effects. LAR was administered in the hospital under sedation with nalbuphine and midazolam. In contrast, lanreotide autogel was administered at the patient's home by a dedicated nurse, and was very well tolerated by both the parents and the children with no need for sedation. In addition, following initiation of lanreotide we were able to wean s.c. octreotide over the course of one month, while in the study using LAR s.c. octreotide was discontinued only after the third injection. Pasireotide treatment has not been reported in CHI, but given its particualr affinity to somatostatin receptor subtypes, it should be investigated in the future. Finally, timing and manner of discontinuation of treatment need to be established. Our experience has been that patients with SUR1 mutations by and large respond to medical therapy and tend to remit after several years so that treatment becomes easier with time, and before age 12 years, all medicines can be stopped. With pump therapy, it is easy to gradually reduce the dose of octreotide until it can be stopped altogether. With the long acting analogs, fine-tuning of the dose is technically very difficult, and an alternative approach will have to be found. It is theoretically possible to switch patients form long-acting analogs back to pump therapy for the purpose of weaning; however in our experience patients and family were so content with the monthly injections that they refused to return to the pump.

DEDICATION

This chapter is dedicated to the memory of Prof. Heddy Landau, who treated children with congenital hyperinsulinism for more than 40 years, was involved in deciphering the molecular basis of the disease and pioneered the use of somatostatin analogs in the conservative management of hyperinsulinism. She was our teacher and mentor and will be greatly missed by her colleagues as well as her patients.

REFERENCES

[1]   Brazeau P, Vale W, Burgus R et al. Hypothalamic polypeptide that inhibits the secretion of immunoreactive pituitary growth hormone. *Science* 1973; 179: 77-79.

[2]   Bruns C, Lewis I, Briner U et al. SOM230: a novel somatostatin peptidomimetic with broad somatotropin release inhibiting factor (SRIF) receptor binding and a unique antisecretory profile. *Eur J Endocrinol* 2002; 146: 707-716.

[3]   Patel YC. Somatostatin and its receptor family. *Front Neuroendocrinol* 1999; 20: 157-198.

[4]   Reisine T, Bell GI. Molecular biology of somatostatin receptors. *Endocr Rev* 1995; 16: 427-442.

[5]   Patel YC. Molecular pharmacology of somatostatin receptor subtypes. *J Endocrinol Invest* 1997; 20: 348-367.

[6]   Aynsley-Green A, Hussain K, Hall J et al. Practical management of hyperinsulinism in infancy. *Arch Dis Child Fetal Neonatal Ed* 2000; 82: F98-F107.

[7]   Nestorowicz A, Wilson BA, Schoor KP et al. Mutations in the sulonylurea receptor gene are associated with familial hyperinsulinism in Ashkenazi Jews. *Hum Mol Genet* 1996; 5: 1813-1822.

[8]   de Lonlay P, Fournet JC, Rahier J et al. Somatic deletion of the imprinted 11p15 region in sporadic persistent hyperinsulinemic hypoglycemia of infancy is specific of focal adenomatous hyperplasia and endorses partial pancreatectomy. *J Clin Invest* 1997; 100: 802-807.

[9]   Palladino AA, Stanley CA. A specialized team approach to diagnosis and medical versus surgical treatment of infants with congenital hyperinsulinism. *Semin Pediatr Surg* 2011; 20: 32-37.

[10] Beltrand J, Caquard M, Arnoux JB et al. Glucose metabolism in 105 children and adolescents after pancreatectomy for congenital hyperinsulinism. *Diabetes Care* 2012; 35: 198-203.

[11] Abu-Osba YK, Manasra KB, Mathew PM. Complications of diazoxide treatment in persistent neonatal hyperinsulinism. *Arch Dis Child* 1989; 64: 1496-1500.

[12] Reubi JC, Kappeler A, Waser B et al. Immunohistochemical localization of somatostatin receptor sst2A in human pancreatic islets. *J Clin Endocrinol Metab* 1998; 83: 3746-3749.

[13] Kumar U, Sasi R, Suresh S et al. Subtype-selective expression of the five somatostatin receptors (hSSTR1-5) in human pancreatic islet cells: a quantitative double-label immunohistochemical analysis. *Diabetes* 1999; 48: 77-85.

[14] Arnoux JB, de Lonlay P, Ribeiro MJ et al. Congenital hyperinsulinism. *Early Hum Dev* 2010; 86: 287-294.

[15] Dunne MJ, Petersen OH. Potassium selective ion channels in insulin-secreting cells: physiology, pharmacology and their role in stimulus-secretion coupling. *Biochim Biophys Acta* 1991; 1071: 67-82.

[16] Philippe J. Somatostatin inhibits insulin-gene expression through a posttranscriptional mechanism in a hamster islet cell line. *Diabetes* 1993; 42: 244-249.

[17] Redmon JB, Robertson RP. Iron and diabetes: an attractive hypothesis, but. *Mayo Clin Proc* 1994; 69: 90-92.

[18] Bertherat J, Tenenbaum F, Perlemoine K et al. Somatostatin receptors 2 and 5 are the major somatostatin receptors in insulinomas: an in vivo and in vitro study. *J Clin Endocrinol Metab* 2003; 88: 5353-5360.

[19] Moldovan S, Atiya A, Adrian TE et al. Somatostatin inhibits B-cell secretion via a subtype-2 somatostatin receptor in the isolated perfused human pancreas. *J Surg Res* 1995; 59: 85-90.

[20] Zambre Y, Ling Z, Chen MC et al. Inhibition of human pancreatic islet insulin release by receptor-selective somatostatin analogs directed to somatostatin receptor subtype 5. *Biochem Pharmacol* 1999; 57: 1159-1164.

[21] Hirsch HJ, Loo S, Evans N et al. Hypoglycemia of infancy and nesidioblastosis. Studies with somatostatin. *N Engl J Med* 1977; 296: 1323-1326.

[22] Pollak A, Coradello H, Gherardini R et al. Neonatal nesidioblastosis--diagnosis and preoperative management. *Prog Pediatr Surg* 1983; 16: 71-76.

[23]   Bruining GJ, Bosschaart AN, Aarsen RS et al. Normalization of glucose homeostasis by a long-acting somatostatin analog SMS 201-995 in a newborn with nesidioblastosis. *Acta Endocrinol Suppl* (Copenh) 1986; 279: 334-339.

[24]   Delemarre-van de Waal HA, Veldkamp EJ, Schrander-Stumpel CT. Long-term treatment of an infant with nesidioblastosis using a somatostatin analogue. *N Engl J Med* 1987; 316: 222-223.

[25]   Glaser B, Landau H, Smilovici A, Nesher R. Persistent hyperinsulinaemic hypoglycaemia of infancy: long-term treatment with the somatostatin analogue Sandostatin. *Clin Endocrinol* (Oxf) 1989; 31: 71-80.

[26]   Glaser B, Hirsch HJ, Landau H. Persistent hyperinsulinemic hypoglycemia of infancy: long-term octreotide treatment without pancreatectomy. *J Pediatr* 1993; 123: 644-650.

[27]   Thornton PS, Alter CA, Katz LE et al. Short- and long-term use of octreotide in the treatment of congenital hyperinsulinism. *J Pediatr* 1993; 123: 637-643.

[28]   Ludwig A, Ziegenhorn K, Empting S et al. Glucose metabolism and neurological outcome in congenital hyperinsulinism. *Semin Pediatr Surg* 2011; 20: 45-49.

[29]   Mazor-Aronovitch K, Gillis D, Lobel D et al. Long-term neurodevelopmental outcome in conservatively treated congenital hyperinsulinism. *Eur J Endocrinol* 2007; 157: 491-497.

[30]   Adamkin DH. Postnatal glucose homeostasis in late-preterm and term infants. *Pediatrics* 2011; 127: 575-579.

[31]   Murray RD, Melmed S. A critical analysis of clinically available somatostatin analog formulations for therapy of acromegaly. *J Clin Endocrinol Metab* 2008; 93: 2957-2968.

[32]   Hofland LJ, Lamberts SW. The pathophysiological consequences of somatostatin receptor internalization and resistance. *Endocr Rev* 2003; 24: 28-47.

[33]   Lamberts SW, van der Lely AJ, Hofland LJ. New somatostatin analogs: will they fulfil old promises? *Eur J Endocrinol* 2002; 146: 701-705.

[34]   Schmid HA. Pasireotide (SOM230): development, mechanism of action and potential applications. *Mol Cell Endocrinol* 2008; 286: 69-74.

[35]   Gillis JC, Noble S, Goa KL. Octreotide long-acting release (LAR). A review of its pharmacological properties and therapeutic use in the management of acromegaly. *Drugs* 1997; 53: 681-699.

[36] Heron I, Thomas F, Dero M et al. Pharmacokinetics and efficacy of a long-acting formulation of the new somatostatin analog BIM 23014 in patients with acromegaly. *J Clin Endocrinol Metab* 1993; 76: 721-727.

[37] Caron P, Beckers A, Cullen DR et al. Efficacy of the new long-acting formulation of lanreotide (lanreotide Autogel) in the management of acromegaly. *J Clin Endocrinol Metab* 2002; 87: 99-104.

[38] Bronstein M, Musolino N, Jallad R et al. Pharmacokinetic profile of lanreotide Autogel in patients with acromegaly after four deep subcutaneous injections of 60, 90 or 120 mg every 28 days. *Clin Endocrinol* (Oxf) 2005; 63: 514-519.

[39] Ben-Shlomo A, Melmed S. Somatostatin agonists for treatment of acromegaly. *Mol Cell Endocrinol* 2008; 286: 192-198.

[40] Krassas GE. Ophthalmic complications in juvenile Graves' Disease - clinic and therapeutic approaches. *Pediatr Endocrinol Rev* 2003; 1 Suppl 2: 223-229; discussion 229.

[41] Colao A, Pivonello R, Di Somma C et al. Growth hormone excess with onset in adolescence: clinical appearance and long-term treatment outcome. *Clin Endocrinol* (Oxf) 2007; 66: 714-722.

[42] Tajima T, Tsubaki J, Ishizu K et al. Case study of a 15-year-old boy with McCune-Albright syndrome combined with pituitary gigantism: effect of octreotide-long acting release (LAR) and cabergoline therapy. *Endocr J* 2008; 55: 595-599.

[43] Kessler M, David R, Pawelczak M et al. Thyrotropin-secreting pituitary adenoma in an adolescent boy: challenges in management. *Pediatrics* 2010; 126: e474-478.

[44] Lustig RH, Hinds PS, Ringwald-Smith K et al. Octreotide therapy of pediatric hypothalamic obesity: a double-blind, placebo-controlled trial. *J Clin Endocrinol Metab* 2003; 88: 2586-2592.

[45] Carel JC, Blumberg J, Bougeard-Julien M et al. Long-acting lanreotide in adolescent girls with constitutional tall stature. *Horm Res* 2009; 71: 228-236.

[46] Bakker B OW. Diagnosis and management of congenital hyperinsulinism: a case report. *Eur J Endocrinol* 2006; 155: S153–S155.

[47] Modan-Moses D, Koren I, Mazor-Aronovitch K et al. Treatment of congenital hyperinsulinism with lanreotide acetate (Somatuline Autogel). *J Clin Endocrinol Metab* 2011; 96: 2312-2317.

[48] Le Quan Sang KH, Arnoux JB, Mamoune A et al. Successful treatment of congenital hyperinsulinism with long-acting release octreotide. *Eur J Endocrinol* 2012; 166: 333-339.

In: Somatostatin   ISBN: 978-1-62417-419-3
Editors: A. Anderson and T. McAnulty © 2013 Nova Science Publishers, Inc.

Chapter 4

SOMATOSTATIN AND ITS RECEPTORS IN THE MAMMALIAN COCHLEA

Vesna Radojevic and Daniel Bodmer

Department of Biomedicine and the Clinic for Otorhinolaryngology,
Basel, Switzerland

ABSTRACT

Somatostatins (SST) form a family of cyclopeptides that are mainly produced by normal endocrine, gastrointestinal, immune and neuronal cells, as well as by certain tumors. By binding to G-protein-coupled receptors (SSTR1-5) on target cells, SST act as neuromodulators and neurotransmitters, as well as potent inhibitors of various secretory processes and cell proliferation. Little is known about the expression and function of the somatostatinergic system in the mammalian cochlea. We analyzed the expression of SSTR1-SSTR5 in the immature mammalian cochlea. The peak in the expression of SSTR1 and SSTR2 at mRNA and protein level is around the onset of hearing to airborne sound, at postnatal day (P)14. This suggests their involvement in the maturation of the mammalian cochlea. In immunohisochemical studies we demonstrated that all five receptors are expressed in the outer and inner hair cells (HCs) as well as in defined supporting cells of the organ of Corti (OC) in the adult mouse cochlea. A similar expression of the SST receptors in the inner and outer hair cells was found in cultivated P6 mouse OC explants. Interestingly, SST itself is not expressed in the mammalian cochlea, suggesting that SST reaches its receptors either trough the blood-labyrinthine barrier from the systemic circulation or via the endolymphatic duct from the endolymphatic sac. In order to learn more about the regulation of SST receptors, we used mice with either a deletion of SSTR1, SSTR2 or SSTR1/SSTR2. In SSTR1 knock-out (KO) mice, SSTR2 were up-regulated. In contrast, in SSTR2 KO mice, the expression pattern of SSTR1 was not altered compared to wild-type mice. In SSTR1/SSTR2 double knockout (DKO) mice, SSTR5 was up-regulated but SSTR3 and SSTR4 were down regulated. These findings provide evidence of a compensatory regulation in the mammalian cochlea as a consequence of a receptor subtype deletion. In addition, we observed reduced levels of phospho-Akt and total-Akt in SSTR1 KO and DKO mice as compared to wild type (WT) mice. Akt is likely to be involved in hair cell survival.

Most importantly, we found improved hair cell survival in somatostatin treated OC explants that had been exposed to gentamicin compared to those explants exposed to gentamicin alone. These findings propose that the somatostatinergic system within the cochlea has neuroprotective properties.

INTRODUCTION

SST, a regulatory peptide with two bioactive forms, SST-14 and SST-28, is produced in neuroendocrine cells in the brain and periphery and acts on a wide array of tissue targets to modulate neurotransmission, cell secretion, and cell proliferation [1], [2]. The discovery of somatostatin receptor subtypes triggered in depth research into their binding properties and coupling to multiple signaling pathways. SST acts via a family of G-protein-coupled receptors (SSTR1-SSTR5), which are differentially distributed throughout the central nerve system (CNS) [3]. Signaling through somatostatin receptors is complex and involves auto-, para-, or endocrine mechanisms [4], [5], [6], [7], [8].

Based on their sequence homology, the receptor subtypes can be placed into two subgroups. The classification is based on structural features and strongly supported by their pharmacological properties. The first receptor group comprises SSTR2, SSTR3 and SSTR5 while SSTR1 and SSTR4 belong to the second group.

The studies published are broadly in agreement and suggested that all the SST receptor types are widespread throughout the brain. The five SSTRs are variably expressed in the brain. In the rat, mRNA for SSTR1 is the most abundant followed by SSTR2, SSTR5, SSTR3 and SSTR4 [1], [9], [10], [11].

In mammalian, all five subtypes of SSTRs are expressed also in the retina. They are distributed to specific retinal cell populations, including subtypes of photoreceptor, bipolar, amacrine and ganglion cells [12], [13]. Most SSTR subtypes have been shown to modulate voltage-gated Ca^{2+} channels as well as glutamate receptor channels in several organ systems [14]. Excessive Ca^{2+} influx into cells is thought to be a major contributor to cell death in ischemic and excitotoxic models of neuronal injury [15]. Binding of somatostatin to its receptors induces G-protein activation through various pathways. As a consequence, the activation of several key enzymes, including adenylyl cyclase, phosphothyrosine phosphatase (PTPase) and mitogen activated protein kinase (MAPK) are modulated along with changes in the intracellular levels of calcium and potassium ions [16]. Studies over the last few years in mice show that SST and its receptors appear to play an important role in cell death. However, in contrast to the situation in the brain and retina, only little information is available on the expression or function of SST and its receptors in the inner ear and auditory system. Tachibana at el. reported on SST-like immunoreactivity in the medial geniculate body, cochlear nucleus, inferior colliculus, auditory cortex and in the cochlea [17]. Tachibana did not find SST-like immunoreactivity in the cochlear perilymph. Also, SST-like immunoreactivity could be observed in the cochlear nuclei of postnatal rats and it was suggested that somatostatin might be important for the development of the auditory system [18]. In an additional study, SST producing cells could be observed in the covering epithelium of the spiral prominence and in the epithelium of the intermediate and rugosal part of the endolymphatic sac [19] [20].

In recent studies from our group, we demonstrated expression of SSTR1 and SSTR2 mRNA in the postnatal rat cochlea and we reported on a dose-dependent protective effect of somatostatin on gentamicin-induced HC loss in vitro [21].

The present review will focus on the relevant aspects of SSTRs expression during development and in the mature mouse cochlea. In addition, to providing a summary of previously published data, it provides information concerning recent and unpublished data from our laboratory, in particular focusing on recent studies using cochlea of mice carrying genetic deletion of the SSTR1, SSTR2 and deletion of both SSTR1 and SSTR2 as experimental models. Finally, the evidence will be reviewed supporting a possible role of SST in maturation of the cochlea and for the hearing process.

SOMATOSTATINERGIC SYSTEM AND COCHLEAR DEVELOPMENT

The mammalian inner ear is an unusually complex organ that contains both vestibular and auditory parts. The vestibular sensory organs are necessary for the maintenance of normal balance. The coiled cochlea containing the OC consists of four parallel rows of sensory HCs along the longitudinal axis of the spiraled cochlea.

The first row of HCs from the center (or medial side) of the cochlea are known as IHC. The remaining three rows of HCs toward the periphery (or lateral side) of the cochlea are known as OHC. Invariably, HCs are separated from each other by several types of morphologically distinct non-sensory supporting cells, including Deiter's cells (DeC), Claudius cells, Boettcher cells, and pillar cells (PiC).

Supporting cells share a common progenitor with HCs [22], and are a morphologically diverse population of epithelial cells that surround HCs and provide structural and functional support.

Gross anatomical changes of the inner ear have been correlated with the appearance of each sensory organ. In turn, the appearance of each organ has been identified by the observation of specific gene expression in sensory regions before histological differentiation. The Notch signaling pathway has multiple roles during inner ear development [23], [24].

Notch signaling activates the transcription of Hes5, a homologue of Drosophila hairy and enhancer of split proteins that encodes a basic helix-loop-helix transcriptional repressor. Previous studies have shown that Hes5 is expressed in the cochlea during embryonic development [25], [26] [27].

SST is a potential candidate for influencing early neuronal development, since the neuropeptide is transiently expressed in several neuronal systems. SSTR3, 4, and 5 have not been shown to be essential for the function of SST [7].

Therefore, first we focused our attention on the distributions of SSTR1 and SSTR2. SSTR1 and SSTR2 positive cells can be observed in fetal mice as early as E14, and become present in all principal neurosensory cochlear cells before birth.

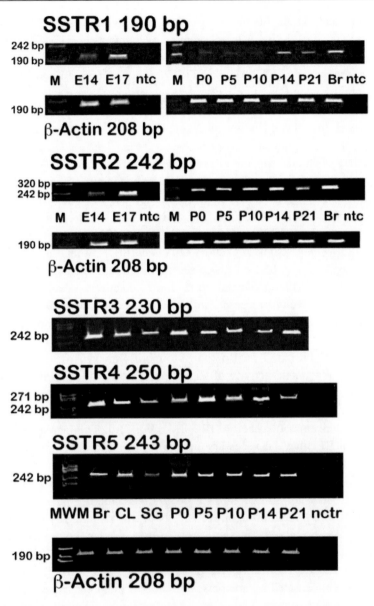

Figure 1. Gene expression of SSTR1- 5, in the in the OC explants at different embryonic and postnatal ages. All five receptors mRNA was detected in the OC of wild-type mice by RT-PCR with the use of specific primer sets at E14, E17 and P0, P5, P10, P14, and P21. Gene expression of SSTR3, -4 and 5, was also detected in the cell lysate (CL) of neuroepithelial cells, spiral ganlion SG and Brain (Br), which RNA was used as a positive control. Omission of RT-PCR was used as the no template control (ntc). β-actin was used to control cDNA synthesis. Molecular weight marker (MWM).

During maturation of the hearing organ, SSTR1 and SSTR2 were expressed in cochlea during late embryonic development.

In the period of cochlear extension and coiling (until approximately E19-P0) the expression of SSTR1 and SSTR2 receptors increased and continued throughout the maturation of OC (Figure 1).

The high expression of both receptors at E17 supports the differentiation of the neuroepithelial cells in the embryonic OC, as well as general growth and development of the inner ear.

A variety of studies support a developmental role for SST by documenting its early onset, transient expression, and morphogenetic effects [28], [29]. Transient expression of SST protein or mRNA has been described in the cerebellum [30], the cerebral cortex [31], and in sensory systems, including the somatosensory, visual [32], and auditory systems [33]. Recent studies have shown that SST exerts some regulatory effects during neuronal maturation, as it has been reported that SST enhances neurite outgrowth in cultured cerebellar neurons [34]. In the postnatal period of cochlear development the immunoreactivity of both receptors increases until approximately P14 at the onset of hearing. During this postnatal period maximal labeling of the IHC, OHC, and supporting cells is reached for both receptors, and subsequently decreases by P21 [58]. SST is also known to modify the synapses and is likely to influence the synaptic activity of the inner ear at P14 [35], [36] [37]. Like other rodent species, mice do not respond to airborne sound shortly after birth. The outer ear canal remains closed until P12, and auditory brainstem responses cannot be reliably recorded before P12-P14 [38], [39]. The increase of these proteins until P14 may be necessary for the growth and development of the OC, although not for mature hearing.

In addition, it is noteworthy that the developmental pattern of SSTR1 and SSTR2 expression are similar to each other. Interestingly, there is a strong correlation of mRNA and protein levels for both SSTR1 and SSTR2 receptor, suggesting that SSTRs expression in the inner ear is controlled at the transcriptional level (Figure 1).

In our previous publication we observed that deletion of one receptor subtype was compensated by an over-expression of the other receptor subtype [40]. These findings support the idea that both receptors have related functions in the inner ear. After P14, major anatomical structures and connections are already present. The expression of SSTR1 and SSTR2 at P21 is decreased relative to P14. The distribution patterns of SSTR1 and SSTR2 at P21 were similar to those observed in adult mice after airborne hearing ability has commenced. From brain studies it is suggested that the SSTR1 and SSTR2 appear relatively early in the development. It has been suggested that during brain development SST may be involved in synaptogenesis, proliferation, axon pathfinding, and/or as a tropic factor [41]. Furthermore because of the high expression level of SSTR1 and SSTR2 in the cochlea at age P14 they may not only be involved in proliferation but also in synaptogenesis.

SOMATOSTATIN AND LOCALIZATION OF SOMATOSTATIN RECEPTORS IN THE MAMMALIAN COCHLEA

Many studies suggested that all SSTRs types widespread throughout the brain and are variably expressed in the rat [1], [9], [11], [10]. The distribution of the mRNA expression for all five SSTRs types has been investigated extensively using different technique in the rat and human [42], [10]. At present, very little is known about the expression of SSTRs receptors in the inner ear.

Our recent observation in mouse cochlea show that all SSTRs were expressed at mRNA and protein level. In the cochlea of adult mice SSTR1 immunorecativity was observed in apical part of the OHC and IHC, inner PiC, and spinal ganglion (SG) [40].

SSTR2 immunoreactivity was observed in the IHC and OHC with strong intensity in the PiC and DeC (Table 1A). According to the labeling with neurofilament marker SMI3, the cochlear afferent neurons do not expressed SSTR1 and SSTR2 [40].

Furthermore, in our studies we demonstrate that the SSTR3-5 are specifically expressed in OHC and IHC of the OC, as well as in defined supporting cells.

Expression of SSTR3 in mouse cochlea with prominent immunostaining was detected in the basal part of OHC, apical part of IHC as well as in cell bodies of SG cells (Figure 2A). (Table 1B). The SSTR3 immunoreactivity was widely distributed throughout the human bran, being particularly enriched in the cortex, hippocampus, the amigdala, the hippothalamus and cerebellum [43]. Analysis at the fluorescence microscopic level revealed and exclusive localization of SSTR4 at supporting cells of OHC (Figure 2B). Also strong signal was detected at the apical part of IHC. The SG shows a strong signal in the cell body of all type of ganglion cells. Immunohistochemistry on adult rat brain section showed the SSTR4 to have a common distribution in cell body as well as neuronal processes in the cerebral cortex, hippocampus and several nuclei in the brainstem [44]. The study of Schreff et al. showed that SSTR4 was strictly somatodendritic and most likely functions in a postsynaptic manner. The SSTR4 may have a previous unappreciated function during the neuronal degeneration-regeneration process [45]. SSTR5 immunoreactivity showed an overall distribution in OC with strong immunostaining in the apical and basal part of OHC and apical part of IHC (Figure 2C). The expression of SSTR1-and 2 in cultivated P5 mouse OC explants was similar to their expression in IHC and OHC [40].

Table 1. Regional distribution of SSTR1-5 in the mouse cochlea determined by immunohistochemistry. The table lists relative densities of SSTRs signals in cochlear structures

A

	SST1 immunoreactivity							SST2 immunoreactivity					
	Embryonic OC	Supporting cells	IHC	OHC	PiC	DeC		Embryonic OC	Supporting cells	IHC	OHC	PiC	DeC
E14	+	++					E14	++	+++				
E17	+++	++					E17	+++	+				
P0			+++	+++	+	+	P0			+++	+++	++	++
P5			++	++	++	++	P5			++	+++	++	++
P10			++	+++	+++	+++	P10			++	+++	+++	+++
P14			+	+	+++	++	P14			++	+++	++	+++
P21			+	+	+	+++	P21			+	+	++	+++

+ weak, ++ moderate, +++ strong

B

SSTR1-5 Immunoreactivity

	Area			
SSTRs	IHC	OHC	PiC	DeC
SSTR3	+++	++	++	+++
SSTR4	++	+	+	+++
SSTR5	+++	+++	+	++

+ weak, ++ moderate, +++ strong

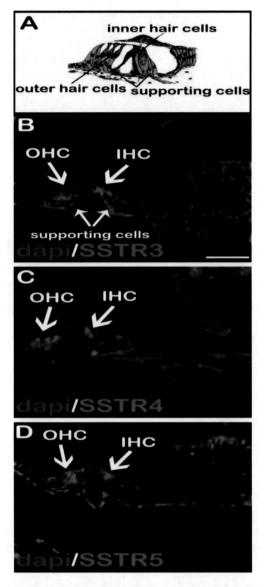

Figure 2. The protein expression profile of SSTR3, -4 and 5 in the adult mouse cochlea. A, The diagram of OC source : http://syllabus.med.unc.edu. B, The protein expression of SSTR3 (red) in the OC can be detected in IHC and OHC included the supporting cells of OHC; cell nuclei (Dapi) are in blue. C, SSTR4 immunolabeling was prominent in the supporting cells of OHC but was also detected in the IHC and OHC. D, SSTR5 immunolabeling in the mouse cochlea was in the OC and SG. Strong signal of SSTR5 was detected in IHC and OHC. All images by immunofluorescence microscopy, scale bar = 100 μm.

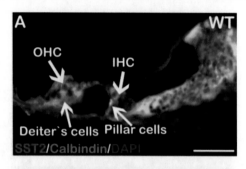

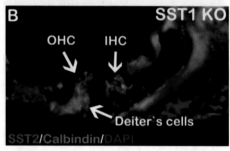

Figure 3. Cochlear SSTR2 localization in WT and SST1 KO mice. A, detection of SSTR2 in cochlea of WT mice. SSTR2 (red) in WT is expressed in IHC and OHC. B, SSTR (red) was detected in OHC and Deiter`s cells in SSTR1 KO cochlea. Cell nuclei (DAPI, blue) and calbindin staining (green). Images by fluorescence microscopy; scale bar = 100 µm.

The SSTR1-5 proteins are also expressed in passaged cochlear neurosensory cells derived from postnatal mouse OC [40] (for SSTR3, -4 and 5 (data not shown). SSTR5 was prominent expressed in the basal forebrain, suggesting that they may be involved in the mediation of somatostatin effects on the sleep-wake cycle through their association with cortically projecting subcortical systems [46].

In the retina, the labeling for SSTR5 was restricted to the inner retina and the labeling was seen almost in GABAergic amacrine cells (AC), including dopaminergic and cholinergic AC, but not glycinergic cells (AII AC) [47]. All five subtypes of SSTRs are expressed in the mammalian retina. There are distributed to specific retinal cell population, including subtypes of photoreceptor, bipolar, amacrine and ganglion cells [12].

Somatostatin itself was not expressed in the mammalian cochlea, suggesting that somatostatin reaches its receptors either through the blood-labyrinthine barrier from the systemic circulation or via the endolymphatic duct from the endolymphatic sac.

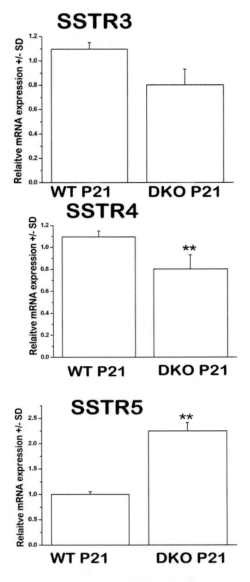

Figure 4. SSTR3, -4 and 5 cochlear gene expression in OC explants P21 of wild type and DKO mice. The relative distribution of SSTR3, -4 and 5 mRNA expression in OC tissue from wild-type and DKO mice of different postnatal ages was quantified by real-time PCR. GAPDH was used as an endogenous control. Gene expression levels are expressed as mean (± S.E.) fold increase as compared with values obtained in OC explants from P21 mice from WT and DKO. Data were obtained from 5 independent experiments. Statistical analysis was performed using the student t-test. ** p<0.004.

SOMATOSTATIN RECEPTORS IN COCHLEA
OF KNOCK OUT MICE

The KO and DKO mice in which SSTR1 and SSTR2 are knocked out have been generated and used to investigate the biological consequences of the absence of SSTRs [48], [49]. These KO and DKO do not exhibit major phenotypic defects or main behavioral impairments [3], [49], [48]. Immunohistochemisty in SSTR1 KO cochlea shows that SSTR2 was increased. SSTR2 protein was strongly expressed in DeC, and to a lesser extent in OHC, but was absent from PiC and IHC compared with WT mice (Figure 3). In SSTR2 KO the staining pattern did not differ from that of WT mice [40]. In addition, no major compensatory regulation of SST or individual SSTRs has been described as a consequence of the genetic deletion of SSTR1 or SSTR2 in specific brain regions [50]. In the retina, recently major alterations of SST content were demonstrated as a consequence of SSTR1 or SSTR2 deletion [51], [52]. Indeed, SSTR1 loss causes an increased expression of SSTR2 [40]. In the DKO mouse cochlea the expression of SSTR3 mRNA, as measured with quantitative qPCR in OC explants from P21 day-old mice was not significantly changed but the expression of SSTR4 in OC explants from P21 day-old mice was significantly decreased compared to age matched OC explants from WT mice. SSTR5 mRNA was expressed at a significantly higher level compared to WT cochlea (Figure 4). Our findings demonstrate prominent compensatory regulation in the mammalian cochlea as a consequence of distinct SSTRs deletions. This compensatory mechanism is subtype-specific, as it is observed only after the deletion of SSTR1, SSTR1/SSTR2 but not after the deletion of SST2 [40].

ROLE OF SOMATOSTATIN IN PROTECTING
THE INNER EAR

The function of these five receptors in the OC is currently unknown. However, we have recently demonstrated that SST can protect HCs from aminoglycoside toxicity in a dose-dependent manner *in vitro* [21]. It is reasonable to assume that this neuroprotective effect of SST on HCs was mediated by SSTRs; however, this has not yet been experimentally proven. Nevertheless, our findings are consistent with a neuroprotective role for the SST signaling system with respect to auditory HCs. In contrast to the situation in the inner ear, more is known about the expression and neuroprotective role of the somatostatinergic system in the retina. It has been demonstrated that SST and its receptors (SSTR1-SSTR5) are expressed in the retina, predominatly in amacrine cells and bipolar cells [29]. Activation of the SSTR2 by somatostatin or its analogues has been shown to protect retinal neurons against ischemia-induced damage [14]. In addition, studies in mice with genetic alterations of the somatostatinergic system have revealed that an increased presence of functional SSTR2 protects against retinal ischemia. Therefore, SST2 analogues might be of therapeutic benefit in retinal diseases such as glaucoma or diabetic retinopathy, but may also protect from hearing loss due to HC degeneration and death. Studies in mouse retinal explants have demonstrated that the SST2 receptor inhibits potassium-induced glutamate release [53]. By limiting the amount of glutamate available to glutamate receptors, somatostatin and its analogues may exert a neuroprotective function against glutamate neurotoxicity, which characterizes many retinal diseases [5]. Glutamate excitotoxicity appears to be mediated by the activation of caspase-3, as shown in cortical neurons [54]. Glutamate excitotoxicity is also involved in HC damage and death in the cochlea [55]. Therefore, somatostatin may protect HCs from aminoglycoside toxicity, either by limiting glutamate release or by mitigating the toxic action of excess glutamate on HCs. In this context, it is notable that the somatostatin analogue octreotide alters the activity of the phosphatidylinositol 3-kinase pathway in pituitary tumor cells [56]. We demonstrated recently that the phosphatidylinositol 3-kinase pathway is involved in NF-kappaB-dependent HC survival [57]. Therefore, it might be possible that somatostatin exerts its effect on HCs through the phosphatidylinositol 3-kinase survival pathway. Our analysis of levels of phospho-Akt and total Akt protein in WT, SSTR1 KO, and DKO mice demonstrated that deletion of the receptors results in reduced levels of phospho- Akt and total Akt in the KO mice compared with WT mice [58]. Therefore, we can speculate that the protective role of SST on gentamicin-induced HC loss is due to the influence of SST at the PI3K/Akt pathway.

CONCLUSION

In this review we have presented evidence for complex mechanisms by which the expression of the SSTRs in the highly differentiated cochlear tissue is closely interrelated. SSTRs are expressed in cochlea during late embryonic development. In the period of cochlear extension the expression of SSTR1 and

SSTR2 receptors increased and continued throughout the maturation of OC. Our studies support a developmental role for SST by documenting its early onset, expression, and morphogenetic effects. The presence of SSTR1-5 within the mammalian cochlea, their specific expression in the OC, and their subtype-specific compensatory regulation as a consequence of distinct somatostatin receptor deletion as well as its effect on the PI3K/Akt pathway suggest an important role for the somatostatinergic system within the inner ear. Additional studies are needed to clarify to what extent SSTR play an essential role during the development of cochlear neural structures, and which transduction mechanisms are involved given the activation of specific SST receptor subtypes.

REFERENCES

[1] Patel YC: Somatostatin and its receptor family. *Front Neuroendocrinol.* 1999, 20(3):157-198.

[2] Epelbaum J, Dournaud P, Fodor M, Viollet C: The neurobiology of somatostatin. *Crit. Rev. Neurobiol.* 1994, 8(1-2):25-44.

[3] Olias G, Viollet C, Kusserow H, Epelbaum J, Meyerhof W: Regulation and function of somatostatin receptors. *J. Neurochem.* 2004, 89(5):1057-1091.

[4] Dockray GJ, Varro A, Dimaline R: Gastric endocrine cells: gene expression, processing, and targeting of active products. *Physiol. Rev.* 1996, 76(3):767-798.

[5] Epelbaum J: Somatostatin in the central nervous system: physiology and pathological modifications. *Prog Neurobiol* 1986, 27(1):63-100.

[6] Reisine T: Somatostatin. Cell Mol Neurobiol 1995, 15(6):597-614.

[7] Reisine T: Somatostatin receptors. *Am. J. Physiol.* 1995, 269(6 Pt 1):G813-820.

[8] Schindler M, Humphrey PP, Emson PC: Somatostatin receptors in the central nervous system. *Prog. Neurobiol.* 1996, 50(1):9-47.

[9] Breder CD, Yamada Y, Yasuda K, Seino S, Saper CB, Bell GI: Differential expression of somatostatin receptor subtypes in brain. *J. Neurosci.* 1992, 12(10):3920-3934.

[10] Kong H, DePaoli AM, Breder CD, Yasuda K, Bell GI, Reisine T: Differential expression of messenger RNAs for somatostatin receptor subtypes SSTR1, SSTR2 and SSTR3 in adult rat brain: analysis by RNA

blotting and in situ hybridization histochemistry. *Neuroscience* 1994, 59(1):175-184.

[11] Thoss VS, Perez J, Duc D, Hoyer D: Embryonic and postnatal mRNA distribution of five somatostatin receptor subtypes in the rat brain. *Neuropharmacology* 1995, 34(12):1673-1688.

[12] Thermos K: Functional mapping of somatostatin receptors in the retina: a review. *Vision Res.* 2003, 43(17):1805-1815.

[13] Vasilaki A, Thermos K: Somatostatin analogues as therapeutics in retinal disease. *Pharmacol. Ther.* 2009, 122(3):324-333.

[14] Celiker U, Ilhan N, Ozercan I, Demir T, Celiker H: Octreotide reduces ischaemia-reperfusion injury in the retina. *Acta Ophthalmol. Scand.* 2002, 80(4):395-400.

[15] Smaili S, Hirata H, Ureshino R, Monteforte PT, Morales AP, Muler ML, Terashima J, Oseki K, Rosenstock TR, Lopes GS et al: Calcium and cell death signaling in neurodegeneration and aging. *An. Acad. Bras. Cienc.* 2009, 81(3):467-475.

[16] Barnett P: Somatostatin and somatostatin receptor physiology. *Endocrine* 2003, 20(3):255-264.

[17] Tachibana M, Rothman JM, Guth PS: Somatostatin along the auditory pathway. *Hear Res.* 1979, 1(4):365-368.

[18] Takatsuki K, Sakanaka M, Shiosaka S, Inagaki S, Takagi H, Senba E, Hara Y, Kawai Y, Minagawa H, Iida H et al: Pathways and terminal fields of the cochlearofugal somatostatin tracts of very young rats. *Brain Res.* 1982, 255(4):613-626.

[19] Arnold W, Altermatt HJ, Arnold R, Gebbers JO, Laissue J: Somatostatin (somatostatinlike) immunoreactive cells in the human inner ear. In.: *Arch. Otolaryngol. Head Neck Surg.*; 1986 Sep;: 112(119):934-117.

[20] Arnold W, Arnold R, Altermatt HJ: [Hormone-producing (paracrine) cells in the human labyrinth]. 1985 Jul, 64(7):359-363.

[21] Caelers A, Monge A, Brand Y, Bodmer D: Somatostatin and gentamicin-induced auditory hair cell loss. *Laryngoscope* 2009, 119(5):933-937.

[22] Fekete DM, Muthukumar S, Karagogeos D: Hair cells and supporting cells share a common progenitor in the avian inner ear. *J. Neurosci.* 1998, 18(19):7811-7821.

[23] Kiernan AE, Xu J, Gridley T: The Notch ligand JAG1 is required for sensory progenitor development in the mammalian inner ear. *PLoS Genet* 2006, 2(1):e4.

[24] Brooker R, Hozumi K, Lewis J: Notch ligands with contrasting functions: Jagged1 and Delta1 in the mouse inner ear. *Development* 2006, 133(7):1277-1286.

[25] Shailam R, Lanford PJ, Dolinsky CM, Norton CR, Gridley T, Kelley MW: Expression of proneural and neurogenic genes in the embryonic mammalian vestibular system. *J. Neurocytol.* 1999, 28(10-11):809-819.

[26] Zine A, Aubert A, Qiu J, Therianos S, Guillemot F, Kageyama R, de Ribaupierre F: Hes1 and Hes5 activities are required for the normal development of the hair cells in the mammalian inner ear. *J. Neurosci.* 2001, 21(13):4712-4720.

[27] Lanford PJ, Shailam R, Norton CR, Gridley T, Kelley MW: Expression of Math1 and HES5 in the cochleae of wildtype and Jag2 mutant mice. *J. Assoc. Res. Otolaryngol.* 2000, 1(2):161-171.

[28] Bulloch AG: Somatostatin enhances neurite outgrowth and electrical coupling of regenerating neurons in Helisoma. *Brain Res.* 1987, 412(1):6-17.

[29] Bagnoli P, Dal Monte M, Casini G: Expression of neuropeptides and their receptors in the developing retina of mammals. *Histol. Histopathol.* 2003, 18(4):1219-1242.

[30] Viollet C, Bodenant C, Prunotto C, Roosterman D, Schaefer J, Meyerhof W, Epelbaum J, Vaudry H, Leroux P: Differential expression of multiple somatostatin receptors in the rat cerebellum during development. *J. Neurochem.* 1997, 68(6):2263-2272.

[31] Naus CC, Bloom FE: Immunohistochemical analysis of the development of somatostatin in the reeler neocortex. *Brain Res* 1988, 471(1):61-68.

[32] Ferriero DM, Sheldon RA, Messing RO: Somatostatin enhances nerve growth factor-induced neurite outgrowth in PC12 cells. *Brain Res. Dev. Brain Res.* 1994, 80(1-2):13-18.

[33] Kungel M, Friauf E: Somatostatin and leu-enkephalin in the rat auditory brainstem during fetal and postnatal development. *Anat. Embryol.* (Berl) 1995, 191(5):425-443.

[34] Taniwaki T, Schwartz JP: Somatostatin enhances neurofilament expression and neurite outgrowth in cultured rat cerebellar granule cells. *Brain Res. Dev. Brain Res.* 1995, 88(1):109-116.

[35] Kaneko S, Maeda T, Satoh M: Cognitive enhancers and hippocampal long-term potentiation in vitro. *Behav. Brain Res.* 1997, 83(1-2):45-49.

[36] Pilar G, Gray DB, Meriney SD: Membrane delimited and intracellular soluble pathways in the somatostatin modulation of ACh release. *Life Sci* 1996, 58(22):1979-1986.

[37] Dalezios Y, Lujan R, Shigemoto R, Roberts JD, Somogyi P: Enrichment of mGluR7a in the presynaptic active zones of GABAergic and non-GABAergic terminals on interneurons in the rat somatosensory cortex. *Cereb. Cortex* 2002, 12(9):961-974.

[38] Uziel A, Romand R, Marot M: Development of cochlear potentials in rats. *Audiology* 1981, 20(2):89-100.

[39] Geal-Dor M, Freeman S, Li G, Sohmer H: Development of hearing in neonatal rats: air and bone conducted ABR thresholds. *Hear Res.* 1993, 69(1-2):236-242.

[40] Radojevic V, Hanusek C, Setz C, Brand Y, Kapfhammer JP, Bodmer D: The somatostatinergic system in the mammalian cochlea. *BMC Neurosci.* 2011, 12:89.

[41] Bodenant C, Leroux P, Gonzalez BJ, Vaudry H: Transient expression of somatostatin receptors in the rat visual system during development. *Neuroscience* 1991, 41(2-3):595-606.

[42] Harrington KA, Schindler M, Humphrey PP, Emson PC: Expression of messenger RNA for somatostatin receptor subtype 4 in adult rat brain. *Neurosci Lett.* 1995, 188(1):17-20.

[43] Hervieu G, Emson PC: Visualisation of somatostatin receptor sst(3) in the rat central nervous system. *Brain Res. Mol. Brain Res.* 1999, 71(2):290-303.

[44] Selmer IS, Schindler M, Humphrey PP, Emson PC: Immunohistochemical localization of the somatostatin sst(4) receptor in rat brain. *Neuroscience* 2000, 98(3):523-533.

[45] Schreff M, Schulz S, Handel M, Keilhoff G, Braun H, Pereira G, Klutzny M, Schmidt H, Wolf G, Hollt V: Distribution, targeting, and internalization of the sst4 somatostatin receptor in rat brain. *J. Neurosci.* 2000, 20(10):3785-3797.

[46] Stroh T, Kreienkamp HJ, Beaudet A: Immunohistochemical distribution of the somatostatin receptor subtype 5 in the adult rat brain: predominant expression in the basal forebrain. *J. Comp. Neurol.* 1999, 412(1):69-82.

[47] Ke JB, Zhong YM: Expression of somatostatin receptor subtype 5 in rat retinal amacrine cells. *Neuroscience* 2007, 144(3):1025-1032.

[48] Zheng H, Bailey A, Jiang MH, Honda K, Chen HY, Trumbauer ME, Van der Ploeg LH, Schaeffer JM, Leng G, Smith RG: Somatostatin receptor subtype 2 knockout mice are refractory to growth hormone-negative feedback on arcuate neurons. *Mol. Endocrinol.* 1997, 11(11):1709-1717.

[49] Kreienkamp HJ, Akgun E, Baumeister H, Meyerhof W, Richter D: Somatostatin receptor subtype 1 modulates basal inhibition of growth hormone release in somatotrophs. *FEBS Lett.* 1999, 462(3):464-466.

[50] Hannon JP, Petrucci C, Fehlmann D, Viollet C, Epelbaum J, Hoyer D: Somatostatin sst2 receptor knock-out mice: localisation of sst1-5 receptor mRNA and binding in mouse brain by semi-quantitative RT-PCR, in situ hybridisation histochemistry and receptor autoradiography. *Neuropharmacology* 2002, 42(3):396-413.

[51] Dal Monte M, Petrucci C, Vasilaki A, Cervia D, Grouselle D, Epelbaum J, Kreienkamp HJ, Richter D, Hoyer D, Bagnoli P: Genetic deletion of somatostatin receptor 1 alters somatostatinergic transmission in the mouse retina. *Neuropharmacology* 2003, 45(8):1080-1092.

[52] Casini G: Neuropeptides and retinal development. *Arch. Ital. Biol.* 2005, 143(3-4):191-198.

[53] Dal Monte M, Cammalleri M, Martini D, Casini G, Bagnoli P: Antiangiogenic role of somatostatin receptor 2 in a model of hypoxia-induced neovascularization in the retina: results from transgenic mice. *Invest Ophthalmol. Vis. Sci.* 2007, 48(8):3480-3489.

[54] Tenneti L, Lipton SA: Involvement of activated caspase-3-like proteases in N-methyl-D-aspartate-induced apoptosis in cerebrocortical neurons. *J. Neurochem.* 2000, 74(1):134-142.

[55] Kopke RD, Coleman JK, Liu J, Campbell KC, Riffenburgh RH: Candidate's thesis: enhancing intrinsic cochlear stress defenses to reduce noise-induced hearing loss. *Laryngoscope* 2002, 112(9):1515-1532.

[56] Theodoropoulou M, Zhang J, Laupheimer S, Paez-Pereda M, Erneux C, Florio T, Pagotto U, Stalla GK: Octreotide, a somatostatin analogue, mediates its antiproliferative action in pituitary tumor cells by altering phosphatidylinositol 3-kinase signaling and inducing Zac1 expression. *Cancer Res.* 2006, 66(3):1576-1582.

[57] Nagy I, Caelers A, Monge A, Bonabi S, Huber AM, Bodmer D: NF-kappaB-dependent apoptotic hair cell death in the auditory system. *Audiol. Neurootol.* 2007, 12(4):209-220.

[58] Bodmer D, Brand Y, Radojevic V: Somatostatin Receptor Types 1 and 2 in the Developing Mammalian Cochlea. *Dev Neurosci* 2012.

In: Somatostatin   ISBN: 978-1-62417-419-3
Editors: A. Anderson and T. McAnulty © 2013 Nova Science Publishers, Inc.

Chapter 5

DIAGNOSTIC ACCURACY OF POSITRON EMISSION TOMOGRAPHY WITH SOMATOSTATIN ANALOGUES IN GASTROENTEROPANCREATIC AND THORACIC NEUROENDOCRINE TUMORS

Giorgio Treglia[*1] *and Barbara Muoio*[2]
[1]Institute of Nuclear Medicine,
Catholic University of the Sacred Heart, Rome, Italy
[2]School of Medicine,
Catholic University of the Sacred Heart, Rome, Italy

ABSTRACT

Introduction: Positron emission tomography (PET) using somatostatin analogues labelled with Gallium-68 is a valuable diagnostic tool for patients with neuroendocrine tumors (NETs).

[*] Corresponding author: Giorgio Treglia, MD, Institute of Nuclear Medicine, Catholic University of the Sacred Heart, Largo Gemelli, 8; zip code:00168, Rome, Italy, Telephone: +39 0630156200; fax: +39 06 30153745, e-mail: giorgiomednuc@libero.it.

Aim of our study is to review published data about the diagnostic performance of PET or PET/computed tomography (PET/CT) in patients with thoracic and/or gastroenteropancreatic (GEP) NETs.

Methods: A comprehensive computer literature search of studies published through October 2011 and regarding PET or PET/CT studies in patients with thoracic and/or GEP NETs was carried out.

Results: Sixteen studies comprising 567 patients were included in this review. The pooled sensitivity and specificity of PET or PET/CT with somatostatin analogues in detecting NETs were 93% (95% confidence interval [95%CI]: 91-95%) and 91% (95%CI: 82-97%), respectively, on a per patient-based analysis. The area under the ROC curve was 0.96.

Conclusions: In patients with suspicious thoracic and/or GEP NETs, PET or PET/CT with radiolabelled somatostatin analogues demonstrated high sensitivity and specificity. These accurate techniques should be considered as first-line diagnostic imaging methods in patients with suspicious thoracic and/or GEP NETs.

Keywords: PET, PET/CT, somatostatin analogues, neuroendocrine tumours, Gallium-68

INTRODUCTION

Epidemiological data show a worldwide increase in the prevalence and incidence of thoracic and gastroenteropancreatic (GEP) neuroendocrine tumours (NETs) in the past few decades, which is probably due to improved methods of detection of these tumors [1,2]. The diagnosis of NETs usually represents a challenge for the clinicians because their small size and variable anatomic location limit their detection using conventional imaging procedures such as computed tomography (CT), ultrasonography (US), and magnetic resonance imaging (MRI). Furthermore, NETs detection could be missed by Fluorine-18-Fluorodeoxyglucose positron emission tomography/computed tomography (FDG PET/CT) due to the common slow metabolic rate of these tumours [3-5].

NETs overexpress somatostatin receptors on their cell surface and this represents the rationale for the use of somatostatin analogues for diagnosis and therapy of these tumours; in fact, somatostatin receptor imaging noninvasively provides data on receptor expression on NETs cells with direct therapeutic implications [3-5].

Somatostatin receptor scintigraphy (SRS), usually performed using Indium-111 DTPA-octreotide, is still considered as the gold standard for staging of NETs [6,7]. However, several clinical studies have clearly demonstrated the superiority of Gallium-68 somatostatin receptor positron emission tomography/computed tomography (SMSR PET/CT) over SRS [3]. Furthermore, a recent study demonstrated that SMSR PET/CT is considerably cheaper than SRS [8]. Currently, the use of SMSR PET/CT is limited to specialized centers as part of clinical trials [3,4]. Nevertheless, it could be hypothesized that SMSR PET/CT will substitute SRS in the clinical practice for the diagnosis of NETs in the near future.

Several studies showed that SMSR PET and PET/CT, using different radiopharmaceuticals (as Gallium-68 DOTANOC, Gallium-68 DOTATOC and Gallium-68 DOTATATE) are accurate imaging methods in the diagnosis of thoracic (mainly pulmonary and thymic) and GEP NETs; nevertheless, a meta-analysis on this topic is still lacking in the literature. Therefore, the purpose of this study is to meta-analyze published data on the diagnostic performance of SMSR PET and PET/CT in patients with thoracic and/or GEP NETs, in order to add evidence-based data in this setting.

METHODS

A comprehensive computer literature search of the PubMed/MEDLINE, Scopus and Embase databases was carried out to find relevant published articles on the diagnostic performance of SMSR PET or PET/CT in patients with thoracic and/or GEP NETs.

The search was updated until October 31st, 2011.

Studies or subsets in studies investigating the diagnostic performance of SMSR PET or PET/CT in patients with thoracic and/or GEP NETs were eligible for inclusion. Only those studies or subsets in studies that satisfied all of the following criteria were included: a) SMSR PET or PET/CT performed in patients with thoracic and/or GEP NETs; b) sample size of at least 8 patients with NET.

The exclusion criteria were: a) articles not within the field of interest of this review; b) review articles, editorials or letters, comments, conference proceedings; c) case reports or small case series (sample size of less than 8 patients with NET); d) articles including only patients with medullary thyroid carcinoma and/or paragangliomas and/or other neural crest derived tumours; e) insufficient data to reassess sensitivity (number of true positive and false negative) and specificity (number of true negative and false positive) on a per patient-based analysis from individual studies; f) duplicate data (in such cases the most complete article was included in the meta-analysis).

Pooled sensitivity and specificity of SMSR PET or PET/CT were calculated on a per patient-based analysis. The sensitivity was determined from the number of true positive and false negative results obtained from individual studies; the specificity was calculated from the number of true negative and false positive results obtained from individual studies. The area under the ROC curve was calculated to measure the accuracy of SMSR PET or PET/CT in patients with thoracic and/or GEP NETs [9].

RESULTS

Literature Search

The comprehensive computer literature search from the PubMed /MEDLINE, Scopus and Embase databases revealed 1822 articles. Reviewing titles and abstracts, 1774 articles were excluded. Forty-eight articles were selected and retrieved in full-text version; no additional study was found screening the references of these articles.

From these 48 articles potentially eligible for inclusion, after reviewing the full-text article, 27 studies were excluded because sensitivity and specificity of SMSR PET or PET/CT could not be calculated on a per patient-based analysis for insufficient data; moreover, 5 articles were excluded for data overlap.

Finally, 16 studies, comprising a total sample size of 567 patients with NETs met all inclusion criteria, and they were included in this pooled analysis [10-25].

Diagnostic Performance

Sensitivity and specificity of SMSR PET or PET/CT on a per patient-based analysis ranged from 72% to 100% and from 67% to 100%, with pooled estimates of 93% (95%CI: 91-95%) and 91% (95%CI: 82-97%), respectively. The area under the ROC curve was 0.96, demonstrating that SMSR PET or PET/CT are accurate diagnostic methods in NETs diagnosis.

DISCUSSION

Somatostatin receptor imaging represents an important topic in NETs diagnosis [3, 26-28]. Evidence-based data from our analysis suggest that SMSR PET and PET/CT are accurate methods in the diagnosis of thoracic and GEP NETs [9]. Several single-center studies using SMSR PET or PET/CT have reported high sensitivity and specificity of these techniques in patients with NETs. However, many of these studies have limited power, analyzing only relatively small numbers of patients. To derive more robust estimates of diagnostic performance of SMSR PET and PET/CT we pooled published studies. A systematic review process was adopted in ascertaining studies; we have attempted to avoid selection bias by including all relevant studies and adopting rigid inclusion criteria in our analysis. Pooled results of our analysis indicate that SMSR PET and PET/CT demonstrate high sensitivity (93%; 95%CI: 91-95%) and high specificity (91%; 95%CI: 82-97%) to detect thoracic and GEP NETs.

Furthermore, the area under the ROC curve value (0.96) demonstrates that SMSR PET and PET/CT are accurate methods for the diagnosis of thoracic and GEP NETs. Nevertheless, possible causes of false positive and false negative results of these imaging methods should be kept in mind. False negative results could be related to small lesions or NETs with a low expression of somatostatin receptors (for example dedifferentiated NETs). On the other hand, false positive results could be related to other diseases; in particular, inflammatory diseases may cause false positive results because activated inflammatory cells may overexpress somatostatin receptors.

SMSR PET and PET/CT were performed in the included studies using three different radiopharmaceuticals (Gallium-68 DOTATOC, Gallium-68 DOTATATE and Gallium-68 DOTANOC) which differ about the binding profile for the five somatostatin receptor subtypes (sst1-5): whereas Gallium-68 DOTATATE is selective for sst2, Gallium-68 DOTATOC binds to sst2 with high affinity and to sst5 with reasonable affinity; finally, Gallium-68 DOTANOC has high affinity to sst2, sst3, and sst5 [3].

We cannot exclude the potential bias derived from pooling the data obtained by using different radiopharmaceuticals; nevertheless, the differences in somatostatin receptor-binding affinities mentioned above have not yet found a direct clinical correlate [3]; some preliminary experiences have demonstrated a difference in NETs detection using the various somatostatin analogues on a per lesion-based analysis [29,30], but a difference on a per patient-based analysis has not yet been demonstrated.

CONCLUSION

In patients with suspected thoracic and/or GEP NETs, SMSR PET and PET/CT demonstrated high sensitivity and specificity. Nevertheless, possible causes of false negative and false positive results should be kept in mind when interpreting the SMSR PET and PET/CT findings. These accurate techniques should be considered as first-line diagnostic imaging methods in patients with suspicious thoracic and/or GEP NETs; however, large multicenter studies are necessary to substantiate the high diagnostic accuracy of SMSR PET and PET/CT in this setting.

REFERENCES

[1]   Faggiano A, Ferolla P, Grimaldi F, Campana D, Manzoni M, Davì MV, Bianchi A, Valcavi R, Papini E, Giuffrida D, Ferone D, Fanciulli G, Arnaldi G, Franchi GM, Francia G, Fasola G, Crino L, Pontecorvi A, Tomassetti P, Colao A. Natural history of gastro-entero-pancreatic and thoracic neuroendocrine tumors. Data from a large prospective and retrospective Italian Epidemiological study: The Net Management Study. *J. Endocrinol. Invest.* (2011) [Epub ahead of print].

[2]   Rindi G, Wiedenmann B. Neuroendocrine neoplasms of the gut and pancreas: new insights. *Nat. Rev. Endocrinol.* 8, 54-64 (2011).

[3]   Ambrosini V, Fani M, Fanti S, Forrer F, Maecke HR. Radiopeptide imaging and therapy in Europe. *J. Nucl. Med.* 52 Suppl 2, 42S-55S (2011).

[4]   Graham MM, Menda Y. Radiopeptide imaging and therapy in the United States. *J. Nucl. Med.* 52 Suppl 2, 56S-63S (2011).

[5]   Rufini V, Calcagni ML, Baum RP. Imaging of neuroendocrine tumors. *Semin. Nucl. Med.* 36, 228-47 (2006).

[6]   Kwekkeboom DJ, Krenning EP, Scheidhauer K, Lewington V, Lebtahi R, Grossman A, Vitek P, Sundin A, Plöckinger U; Mallorca Consensus Conference participants; European Neuroendocrine Tumor Society. ENETS Consensus Guidelines for the Standards of Care in Neuroendocrine Tumors: somatostatin receptor imaging with (111)In-pentetreotide. *Neuroendocrinology.* 90, 184-189 (2009).

[7]   Vinik AI, Woltering EA, Warner RR, Caplin M, O'Dorisio TM, Wiseman GA, Coppola D, Go VL; North American Neuroendocrine

Tumor Society (NANETS). NANETS consensus guidelines for the diagnosis of neuroendocrine tumor. *Pancreas*. 39 ,713-734 (2010).

[8]   Schreiter NF, Brenner W, Nogami M, Buchert R, Huppertz A, Pape UF, Prasad V, Hamm B, Maurer MH. Cost comparison of (111)In-DTPA-octreotide scintigraphy and (68)Ga-DOTATOC PET/CT for staging enteropancreatic neuroendocrine tumours. *Eur. J. Nucl. Med. Mol. Imaging*. 39, 72-82 (2012).

[9]   Treglia G, Castaldi P, Rindi G, Giordano A, Rufini V. Diagnostic performance of Gallium-68 somatostatin receptor PET and PET/CT in patients with thoracic and gastroenteropancreatic neuroendocrine tumours: a meta-analysis. *Endocrine*. 42, 80-87 (2012).

[10]   Hofmann M, Maecke H, Börner R, Weckesser E, Schöffski P, Oei L, Schumacher J, Henze M, Heppeler A, Meyer J, Knapp H. Biokinetics and imaging with the somatostatin receptor PET radioligand (68)Ga-DOTATOC: preliminary data. *Eur. J. Nucl. Med*. 28, 1751-1757 (2001).

[11]   Koukouraki S, Strauss LG, Georgoulias V, Schuhmacher J, Haberkorn U, Karkavitsas N, Dimitrakopoulou-Strauss A. Evaluation of the pharmacokinetics of 68Ga-DOTATOC in patients with metastatic neuroendocrine tumours scheduled for 90Y-DOTATOC therapy. *Eur. J. Nucl. Med. Mol. Imaging*. 33, 460-466 (2006).

[12]   Gabriel M, Decristoforo C, Kendler D, Dobrozemsky G, Heute D, Uprimny C, Kovacs P, Von Guggenberg E, Bale R, Virgolini IJ. 68Ga-DOTA-Tyr3-octreotide PET in neuroendocrine tumors: comparison with somatostatin receptor scintigraphy and CT. *J. Nucl. Med*. 48, 508-518 (2007).

[13]   Buchmann I, Henze M, Engelbrecht S, Eisenhut M, Runz A, Schäfer M, Schilling T, Haufe S, Herrmann T, Haberkorn U. Comparison of 68Ga-DOTATOC PET and 111In-DTPAOC (Octreoscan) SPECT in patients with neuroendocrine tumours. *Eur. J. Nucl. Med. Mol. Imaging* 34, 1617-1626 (2007).

[14]   Kayani I, Bomanji JB, Groves A, Conway G, Gacinovic S, Win T, Dickson J, Caplin M, Ell PJ. Functional imaging of neuroendocrine tumors with combined PET/CT using 68Ga-DOTATATE (DOTA-DPhe1,Tyr3-octreotate) and 18F-FDG. Cancer. 112, 2447-2455 (2008).

[15]   Ambrosini V, Tomassetti P, Castellucci P, Campana D, Montini G, Rubello D, Nanni C, Rizzello A, Franchi R, Fanti S. Comparison between 68Ga-DOTA-NOC and 18F-DOPA PET for the detection of gastro-entero-pancreatic and lung neuro-endocrine tumours. *Eur. J. Nucl. Med. Mol. Imaging*. 35, 1431-1438 (2008).

[16] Ambrosini V, Castellucci P, Rubello D, Nanni C, Musto A, Allegri V, Montini GC, Mattioli S, Grassetto G, Al-Nahhas A, Franchi R, Fanti S. 68Ga-DOTA-NOC: a new PET tracer for evaluating patients with bronchial carcinoid. *Nucl. Med. Commun.* 30, 281-286 (2009).

[17] Kayani I, Conry BG, Groves AM, Win T, Dickson J, Caplin M, Bomanji JB. A comparison of 68Ga-DOTATATE and 18F-FDG PET/CT in pulmonary neuroendocrine tumors. *J. Nucl. Med.* 50, 1927-1932 (2009).

[18] Haug A, Auernhammer CJ, Wängler B, Tiling R, Schmidt G, Göke B, Bartenstein P, Pöpperl G. Intraindividual comparison of 68Ga-DOTA-TATE and 18F-DOPA PET in patients with well-differentiated metastatic neuroendocrine tumours. *Eur. J. Nucl. Med. Mol. Imaging.* 36, 765-770 (2009).

[19] Frilling A, Sotiropoulos GC, Radtke A, Malago M, Bockisch A, Kuehl H, Li J, Broelsch CE. The impact of 68Ga-DOTATOC positron emission tomography/computed tomography on the multimodal management of patients with neuroendocrine tumors. *Ann. Surg.* 252, 850-856 (2010).

[20] Jindal T, Kumar A, Venkitaraman B, Dutta R, Kumar R. Role of (68)Ga-DOTATOC PET/CT in the evaluation of primary pulmonary carcinoids. *Korean J. Intern. Med.* 25, 386-391 (2010).

[21] Krausz Y, Freedman N, Rubinstein R, Lavie E, Orevi M, Tshori S, Salmon A, Glaser B, Chisin R, Mishani E, J Gross D. 68Ga-DOTA-NOC PET/CT imaging of neuroendocrine tumors: comparison with 111In-DTPA-octreotide (OctreoScan®). *Mol. Imaging Biol.* 13, 583-593 (2011).

[22] Srirajaskanthan R, Kayani I, Quigley AM, Soh J, Caplin ME, Bomanji J. The role of 68Ga-DOTATATE PET in patients with neuroendocrine tumors and negative or equivocal findings on 111In-DTPA-octreotide scintigraphy. *J. Nucl. Med.*, 51, 875-882 (2010).

[23] Versari A, Camellini L, Carlinfante G, Frasoldati A, Nicoli F, Grassi E, Gallo C, Giunta FP, Fraternali A, Salvo D, Asti M, Azzolini F, Iori V, Sassatelli R. Ga-68 DOTATOC PET, endoscopic ultrasonography, and multidetector CT in the diagnosis of duodenopancreatic neuroendocrine tumors: a single-centre retrospective study. *Clin. Nucl. Med.* 35, 321-328 (2010).

[24] Ruf J, Schiefer J, Furth C, Kosiek O, Kropf S, Heuck F, Denecke T, Pavel M, Pascher A, Wiedenmann B, Amthauer H. 68Ga-DOTATOC PET/CT of neuroendocrine tumors: spotlight on the CT phases of a triple-phase protocol. *J. Nucl. Med.* 52, 697-704 (2011).

[25] Naswa N, Sharma P, Kumar A, Nazar AH, Kumar R, Chumber S, Bal C. Gallium-68-DOTA-NOC PET/CT of patients with gastroenteropancreatic neuroendocrine tumors: a prospective single-center study. *AJR Am. J. Roentgenol.* 197, 1221-1228 (2011).

[26] Alexandraki KI, Kaltsas G. Gastroenteropancreatic neuroendocrine tumors: new insights in the diagnosis and therapy. *Endocrine.* 41, 40-52 (2012).

[27] Yim KL. Role of biological targeted therapies in gastroenteropancreatic neuroendocrine tumours. *Endocrine.* 40, 181-186 (2011).

[28] Xu H, Zhang M, Zhai G, Zhang M, Ning G, Li B. The role of integrated (18)F-FDG PET/CT in identification of ectopic ACTH secretion tumors. *Endocrine.* 36, 385-391 (2009).

[29] Poeppel TD, Binse I, Petersenn S, Lahner H, Schott M, Antoch G, Brandau W, Bockisch A, Boy C. 68Ga-DOTATOC Versus 68Ga-DOTATATE PET/CT in Functional Imaging of Neuroendocrine Tumors. *J. Nucl. Med.* 52, 1864-1870 (2011).

[30] Wild D, Bomanji BJ, Reubi JC, Maecke HR, Caplin ME, Ell PJ. Comparison of 68Ga-DOTA-NOC and 68Ga-DOTA-TATE PET/CT in the detection of GEP NETs. *Eur. J. Nucl. Med. Mol. Imaging.* 36(suppl 2), S201 (2009).

INDEX

G

H

T

U

V